Confessions
OF A CLOSED MALE

A Story of Spiritual Awakening

KENNETH BYRD CHANCE

ROJAKETAKA PUBLICATIONS
Navarre, Florida

Published by
Rojaketaka Publications
8668 Navarre Parkway
Suite 110
Navarre, FL 32566
firstchance@mindspring.com

Copyright © 1999 by Kenneth Byrd Chance

All rights reserved. No part of this book may be reproduced in any form or by
any means without the prior written permission of the Publisher, excepting
brief quotations used in connection with reviews, written specifically for inclu-
sion in a magazine or newspaper.

Excerpts from "Alcoholics Anonymous" are re-printed by permission from
Alcoholics Anonymous World Services, Inc.

Printed in Canada
1st printing 1999
Library of Congress Catalog Card Number: 95-095198
ISBN: 1-928927-00-9
1. Spirituality 2. Recovery 3. Men's Issues
First Edition

Cover and book design by Jill Dible

– *One* –

THE PARAMEDICS ATTEMPTED TO GET AN IV STARTED IN MY LIFELESS body. They could not find a vein in either arm that would accept their needle. Imagine, my arms with no veins available! Whenever I gave blood, the technicians told me it was no contest, because my large veins were so easy to hit. After weight training in my late teens and a stint in the Marine Corps, I had developed muscular arms and shoulders, and my veins stood out like gopher trails on a golf green. Yet they tried half a dozen times, on both arms and on the tops of my hands before they gave up.

I had been cutting grass that April morning. The high heat and humidity reminded me of August. After finishing the front yard, I went into the house to get a towel to wipe the sweat from my face. I felt lightheaded, so I laid down on the dining room floor. After a few moments, I decided I'd better get up, because the room felt like it was spinning.

I felt heavy and found moving difficult, but something deep inside me said to go upstairs and get into bed. With all the strength I could summon, I pushed up from the floor, stood up, moved one foot toward the stairs and then another until slowly, laboriously, I climbed the stairs, went down the hall and collapsed into my bed. That was my last voluntary move for the next twenty-four hours.

My wife, Sonnie, was at the bathroom mirror getting dressed and said nothing as I entered the room. After a few minutes, I heard her ask if I was okay, but I was unable to respond.

"Did you hear me?" Sonnie asked.

Nothing. I tried to move my lips to reply, but nothing came out.

"Eric, are you asleep already?"

Fear came over me, because I could not answer. I tried to move my arms to signal her, but they would not move; nor would my legs, my feet, my hands, nothing. I was paralyzed, completely unable to move or otherwise respond to Sonnie's questions. I could see her and hear her, but I was unable to respond.

She came over to the bed. "Are you okay?"

I looked at her as if to say "No! and I don't know what's wrong, either!"

"Eric, say something!" Panic filled her face.

A blank stare was all I could give her. I simply could not respond.

"I'm calling nine-one-one!" She ran to the telephone and dialed while I lay there in the bed, fearing I was on my way out. I had come this far in my forty years of life, I thought, only to find out I might be at the end of the line.

From the open bedroom window, I could faintly hear a siren. My mind raced as I frantically thought about all the little things I should have done before I died. The siren got louder and louder as the fire truck turned down our street. I wondered if I had put the lawnmower back in the garage. Maybe I left it on the sidewalk, and it was in the way of the paramedics.

The siren fell silent as the fire truck parked in front of the house. The noise of the diesel engine was clearly a Detroit clatter. I knew that, because I had been a paramedic fifteen years earlier.

The sound of heaving panting, key chains rattling and equipment banging loudly on the walls filled the house as they made their way up the stairs and into the bedroom. "Where is he, Ma'am?" one of the paramedics asked.

Good ole boys, we called them. They had a distinct Southern dialect that was all Georgia. Warm, cordial, unpretentious and simple. I envied the good ole boys. Among them, life seemed less confusing, and your word was better than any law. Even in an emergency, a good ole boy is always polite, a true Southern Gentleman.

"In here," Sonnie replied nervously as she led them to the bedroom. "I thought he was going to sleep, but now he won't answer me, so I called."

Sonnie is always cool and collected, but this time she was shaken. Her trembling voice gave her away.

"What's his name?" The paramedic looked directly at me, but talked to Sonnie, who had moved toward the dresser to get out of their way.

"Eric. Eric Crane." Her forehead wrinkled, and her eyes looked scared, she bit her bottom lip like she always did when she was anxious.

One of the paramedics leaned over me and asked, "Eric, can you hear me?"

I could only look at him. He had a light blue shirt with a shining silver RVFD badge on the front: Roswell Volunteer Fire Department Number 62.

No reply. I wanted to answer, I tried to, but couldn't.

"Mr. Crane, can you get up?" Number 62 leaned toward me. I saw his name tag: R.E. Phillips.

I tried to open my mouth. No response.

"Eric, we need you to talk to us!" R.E. Phillips yelled at me.

"All right, let's get his vitals." He motioned to his partner as he flashed a pen light into my eyes and then checked my pulse. The other guy took my blood pressure. I looked over at his name tag: W.D. Henry. Did W stand for William or Wayne or Woodrow?

"I'm gonna call it in. Go get the backboard. Looks like we'll have to transport him." Phillips radioed the hospital, then turned to Sonnie. "Is he allergic to any medicine?"

Henry moved quickly out of the bedroom as instructed.

"No. Not that I know of. At least I don't recall that he is." Sonnie did her best to keep her composure. The commotion was exacting its toll on her.

He turned back to the radio, "Negative, not allergic to meds," Phillips reported. Meanwhile, Henry returned with two other guys with him. They had white uniform shirts and dark blue trousers. As one of them moved around the bed, I read the patch on his sleeve: North Fulton Regional Hospital. They were the ambulance crew.

Phillips was busy fiddling around with something on the floor. When he stood up, he had a white packet he ripped open. It was a needle. I panicked. I hate needles. That's why I quit being a paramedic; I was never comfortable with administering IVs.

He tried to stick me on my right hand, but it wouldn't take, so he tried the left hand. No luck. He tried my left forearm and then my right. No way. Everyone was standing around by then, and I was scared out of my pants.

"Forget it, Bobby, let's load him up and try it en route." Henry had saved me from another stick by Phillips.

I was scooped up onto the backboard and strapped tight. With a lot of moans and groans, they hoisted me and carried me out of the bedroom, all two hundred and twenty plus pounds and more than six feet of me.

They couldn't make the sharp 'U' turn that leads to the stairs from the hallway. "Go get the chair stretcher," Phillips ordered one of the ambulance attendants. "Let's take him back to the bedroom."

They took me off the backboard and placed me in a chair stretcher, picked me up, and carried me down the steps. Three guys were in front. Henry directed, while the other two each held the chair. Phillips was at the top position, by my head.

When we got to the foyer, they put me on a gurney and rolled me out to the ambulance.

"You can get in the front, Ma'am." One of the ambulance guys took Sonnie's elbow and walked her to the cab. I was loaded into the back and locked in place. This time Henry tried the IV, but his efforts yielded the same results as Phillips' previous attempts. If I could have, I would have grabbed him and yelled "ENOUGH!" and jumped the hell out of there.

By then they had given up trying to communicate with me. They put a couple of sticky patches on my chest to monitor my body and put an oxygen mask on my face to make sure I was getting enough air.

They pulled away from the house and the siren started again. Henry got on the radio to the hospital.

That's when I heard the voice.

"Eric."

Somehow out of all the chaos going on around me at that moment, I heard a still, calm, quiet but piercing voice. Was it real or imagined? None of the paramedics had spoken directly to me since we left the bedroom. I looked over and saw how busy they were with their "paramedic" business. The voice could not have been coming from one of them.

"Eric."

The voice sounded louder the second time, but it did not come from anyone inside the ambulance. What I sensed was a sound from above me, yet it was not a physical sound. I could hear it clearly, coming from within my being.

"Who are you?" I was sort of talking to myself.

"Do not fear, Eric. Everything is fine. We just need to talk to you." The voice spoke serenely, clearly and distinctly. It sounded familiar, as though I had grown up listening to that voice.

"Who are you?"

"I am your Guardian Angel."

"Do you have a name?" Soon I heard "EL," and then I saw letters appear on a movie screen in my head. The letters appeared one at a time, A...B...L...I...E...L. As clearly as if I had read them from a book, I saw the name: Abliel. The name of my Guardian Angel. Abliel.

I don't know exactly how we communicated. I can't explain it, but I heard a voice and responded. A "thought only" conversation was taking place inside my head, but Abliel's tone and speed sounded distinctly different from my own thoughts. He spoke eloquently and clearly. I use small, everyday words, and I tend to ramble. I heard the paramedics talking to one another, but they seemed removed and far away. Abliel felt close and intimate.

"Will I be okay?" I asked, not knowing whether I should go along with the angel bit or not.

"Yes, do not fear. We need to work with you and to prepare you." His calm and loving response felt assuring.

I felt love. Pure, undefiled love. It filled the back of the ambulance. I was in the presence of unconditional love and complete acceptance. It was serene. I felt warmth with a sense of profound peace and was calmed immediately. I no longer feared what was going on. I could not describe what was going on, and to this day I have difficulty expressing how it felt, because words seem one-dimensional. Meeting Abliel transcended all the dimensions I had known as a human being.

"Prepare me for what?"

"For the work you are about to do."

We got to the hospital, and the attendants quickly pulled the gurney from the ambulance. Several medical people dressed in typical hospital garb of funky green pants and tops and paper shoe covers stood in the entry doors waiting to meet us. They spoke in medical jargon to one another as I laid there, still unable to speak or move. I was enveloped in what I can best describe as a cloud of soft light and radiant love.

They wheeled me into a room and pulled the curtains. Six people surrounded me. A nurse made another attempt at inserting an IV. She patiently searched for a vein, finally found one on the top of my hand she could use, inserted a needle and started the IV.

One person put a stethoscope on my chest while another took my blood pressure. Someone else shaved my chest. They applied jelly and stuck patches on my chest and stomach. A technician plugged wires into the patches and a machine began monitoring my heart beat. I could have been an exotic car engine brought in for a computer diagnosis, for all they cared.

Someone grabbed my foot, trying to get a response. He used a device that resembled a pizza cutter, to roll up and down the soles of my bare feet. I could feel it, but I could not respond. He banged below my knee caps with a pink-red rubber mallet and rubbed his knuckles hard across my chest. Still no response. I could not say a word or move a muscle.

Finally a doctor grabbed my hand and looked straight into my eyes. "Mr. Crane, I want you to squeeze my hand as hard as you can." He talked in a loud voice, very deliberately, so that I would understand him.

Nothing. I was embarrassed. I had been the number-one rope climber in my Marine Corps platoon. All that strength, and I could not even squeeze a doctor's hand.

Sonnie was standing by me. The tears in her eyes told me she was scared. I wanted so much to reassure her that everything was going to be all right, but I could not speak.

"Tell her not to worry. Tell her it is okay not to be scared and that everything is okay." Abliel's kind soft words were clear.

"But, I can't talk! How can I tell her that?"

"You can tell her now," he lovingly responded.

I reached my hand up weakly and motioned for her to come over to me. "Sonnie." I was able to faintly whisper her name. "Everything is going to be okay. There is no need to fear." She looked at me in amazement and nodded her head in acknowledgement.

The medical staff continued their work with me while Abliel continued to reassure me.

After all the preliminary testing, someone made a decision to move me to the Coronary Care Unit of the hospital. I lost track of time, so I do not know whether I was in the emergency room for a few minutes or a few hours.

In CCU, the staff hooked me up to more monitors and a second IV. I saw medical people around me, but I remained unable to respond to their questions. All the while, Abliel was still speaking to me.

"You need to learn to love, Eric. You have been brought here because you were too busy to listen to us. You have tried at times to be loving, but you stop the flow before it can work. We were compelled to bring you here so we could get your attention. Everything is okay with you physically. It is necessary for us to stop you to get you to a place where you will listen and be receptive to our message."

A nurse walked in and checked the IV.

"I'm just making sure this IV doesn't come out. They said they had quite a time in ER trying to find a vein that would work." She lifted my hand, examined the needle and returned my hand gently to my side. "Looks okay to me. How are you?"

I gave an affirmative nod.

"I'll be back later." She turned and walked out.

"Abliel? Are you still here?"

"Yes, Eric. I am here. Let me continue. Love is the primary force of the universe, a force greater than you are aware, Love is the energy that creates all that is. Love is the essence of the life spirit. It is the Center of all creation, and all that has been created has been created through the power of Love."

"What?" I did not comprehend his message.

"You do not understand this now, but in time, you will come to understand the true power of Love and how Love is in all things. This message, once understood, must be carried to the world."

"Am I supposed to tell them this?" I thought to myself.

"It is time that the people of this world prepare for that which is to come, the return of the Christ Spirit to Earth. Soon all will come to experience the return of the Christ Spirit personally, and then they may choose for themselves to live in Love or to live in fear. Only then can the planet be healed, for the collective choices of the people will determine the course for the planet."

"But I know nothing about..."

Abliel interrupted my thoughts. "I will show you events that might come to pass, if the consciousness of humanity does not rise in Love."

I saw a major earthquake in Los Angeles. I also saw an explosion in what appeared to be Sacramento. The destruction in both places was devastating and reduced everything to rubble. Little remained. I felt horrified at the vision.

"This is what is to come if the message of Love is not received in the hearts of mankind," Abliel warned. "You must carry this message forth to all you meet, that the hearts may be turned to the Father and Mother of all. The consciousness of the earth must be raised so that the next level of evolution can occur."

"But why me?" I still received no answer as to why I was chosen.

"Christ consciousness is returning to earth, and if man is not ready for it, the force of the earth will release its energy to make itself ready for the new awareness to come. Be prudent and prepare. Destruction can be avoided, but only if the hearts are turned from Ego to Spirit through Love. That is all," Abliel commanded.

"That's all? But, hey what a minute, is that it?"

Silence.

I was tired and fell asleep. I slept well, because the next thing I knew it was five a.m., the lights in the room had been turned on and a lab technician came in to draw blood. She had an easier time locating a vein than the nurse in the ER.

After she left, I laid quietly, thinking about what had happened. Abliel returned and spoke.

"Last night, spiritual healers and surgeons came and worked on you. Through the use of crystals and spiritual surgery, your ethereal body has received a complete healing. This also means all that is physical has been returned to normal."

"There you are, I want to know more about..."

Abliel interrupted again. "You will receive a Teacher, a Spirit Guide. He will spend time with you. Listen closely to him, Eric."

"How will I know who he is through all this confusion?"

"You will know, Eric." A doctor walked into my room as Abliel finished speaking.

"Good morning, Mr. Crane. How do you feel this morning?"

"Much better, thank you." I was amazed I could respond.

"We were unable to find anything wrong with you. Yesterday you were anemic and your white blood cell count was extremely low, but this morning, everything seems normal. I can't explain what happened, but we're going to keep you a few days to monitor things. Any questions?"

"Not now, thanks a lot, though." Abliel had already explained the situation and I really had no questions for the doctor.

Breakfast was brought in, and I ate it all. I grew tired. As I was falling asleep, I felt Abliel's wings enfold me, giving me protection and comfort which helped me sleep soundly.

Later that day, an orderly moved me to a regular room. Abliel was with me the entire time. Sonnie arrived, and we talked.

"Hello, Honey." She liked to call me honey.

"Hi, Wook." My nickname for her. I read that in a Richard Bach book. Its the nickname he used for his wife. I'm not sure how he pronounced it, but the way I did rhymed with book.

"I see you have a new room. How nice." The appearance of a room, even a hospital room, was important to Sonnie.

"Yeah, I even have a view." I gestured to the window.

"So, have you had a chance to rest?" she asked as she peered out the window.

Should I tell her now about Abliel? Might as well. "Sonnie, there's something I need to explain to you. You might want to sit down."

She pulled up the visitor's chair beside the bed. "My, this sounds serious!"

"Well, I suppose it is. When the paramedics came to take me to the hospital, I, uh, well I, uh, oh I don't know how to say this! I had a visit from my Guardian Angel."

Silence filled the room.

She finally spoke. "I see. Does it have a name?" Her eyes were larger than normal and her forehead wrinkled.

"Abliel." I replied, without elaboration.

"Abliel?" Her eyes rolled; her head angled in skepticism.

"Yeah, at least that's the name I got. You see, all the time they were trying to get me stabilized in the back of the ambulance, Abliel was telling me everything was going to be okay, that they merely needed to talk to me, but that I was not listening. To get my attention they shut my system down and put me here." I felt like the Beaver explaining something to Mrs. Cleaver.

"They?" Sonnie said with amazement.

"Abliel and my Spirit Guides." I reasoned.

"I see." She glanced away at the wall.

"No, this is for real!" I proclaimed.

"Okay." She looked back at me, with a forced smile. "So Abliel has been teaching me about love." She smiled as if to oblige me. "Oh, Honey, you've been under a lot of stress lately, and I should probably let you rest for a while."

I could tell she did not fully believe the significance of my story. "Really Wook, it's all very real. I am not dreaming this stuff."

"I'm sure, Honey. I'm sure Gabriel, or whatever his name is, is very real." She took my hand, held it and looked directly into my eyes with a courteous smile.

"Sonnie, it's the truth. I swear it. I don't know why this has happened to me. It has something to do with love."

"Love?" Sonnie ran her fingers softly through my hair. "Oh, Eric, it's not that I don't believe you, it's just that, well, this whole thing has been traumatic, and if you don't mind, I just want to hold you for a while."

"Sure." I pulled back the sheets, let her into the bed, and we snuggled for the first time in weeks. We held each other for a few minutes, realizing we had faced our fears about losing each other through my near-death experience, and perhaps this could be a second chance.

The nurse walked in. "Well, hello you two! Feeling better, Mr. Crane?"

"Very much so, thank you," I answered quickly.

Sonnie started to jump out of the bed.

"Oh that's all right, Sweetie. That's probably the best thing for him right now. You stay right there while I check his vitals."

Sonnie got up anyway, "Well, Honey, I probably should be going. The baby-sitter could only stay for an hour. I'll call you later, okay?" She leaned over and gave me a kiss good-bye.

"Thanks for coming, Wookie. I'll talk to you later."

Sonnie blew me a kiss and walked out.

The nurse checked my blood pressure. "What a cute lady!"

"Thanks. I'm crazy about her." I looked toward the door until she was out of sight. I was always crazy about Sonnie. My heart jumped the first time I saw her, and it jumped then, as I watched her leave.

"I couldn't tell," the nurse said with a wink and a smile. She put her instruments away. "Well, you're okay for now, Mr. Crane. Anything I can get for you?"

"No thanks. I appreciate your asking."

She left and I thought about what Abliel had said. What was going on? Why was I here getting a message like this? Who was my Teacher that was to come?

"Want to know, Eric?" as a voice from the other side of the room interrupted my thoughts.

"Huh?" I looked beyond the monitor and saw an older man facing me. He had wavy, silver-gray hair pulled straight back with no part. His skin was lightly tanned. He had wrinkles on his forehead and crow's feet by his eyes. His face had a firm jaw with a cleft chin. He wore an old fatigue jacket, a red-and-black flannel shirt and well-worn denim jeans. On his feet were an old pair of leather hiking boots that had probably seen more miles than my old Toyota Celica.

"Who are you?" I asked in a whisper that even I barely heard.

"Vida." He answered warmly.

"Are you my teacher?" I asked.

"Teacher? Is that what he called me?" He gazed out the window. "Abliel has high expectations."

"You know Abliel?"

"He's been with you for ages, Eric." He said matter-of-factly.

"What do you mean? I just met him."

"Oh. Well, I'll explain my relationship to Abliel to you later. You and I have much work to do and little time. Did Abliel explain that to you?" Vida moved closer to me.

"He said he needed to get my attention, and that I needed to prepare for something." I minimized what Abliel had told me, not fully trusting what was now happening.

"Yes, go on." He looked into my eyes.

"He talked about love and that I would be sent a teacher. That's about it." Why use a lot of words when a few would suffice, I thought.

"Okay. Let's start with that." Vida moved around to the foot of the bed and sat on the corner of the mattress. "Don't worry, you're the only one who can see me." He winked. "Close your eyes and relax. Take a deep breath, hold it for a moment, and let it out, slowly."

I did as he said.

"Excellent. Now, again. Breathe in, slowly, take a deep breath, that's it, now hold it, good, now let it out slowly."

He had me breathe like that several times. I listened to his voice, a rich baritone, clear and warm. I started to feel relaxed.

"That's it, Eric, just let go. Now, we are going on a little journey together, back in time to your home in Denver, the brick, three-bedroom rancher in Westminster. You were married to Michele at the time. You had just returned from Spokane where Rich Hutchinson made you the job offer. Remember?"

Yes, I remembered. It was one of those offers you can't turn down, or at least I couldn't. Systech Systems had flown me to its corporate office in Spokane, Washington, to offer me a position as director of distributor sales. The job had all the right ingredients, six-figure salary, prestigious title, executive office with a view of the city skyline and a mahogany desk with matching credenza and bookcase. The new leather executive chair smelled like a million bucks. The parking garage would have an executive spot exclusively for me, complete with my name on it: "E. Crane." Finally, the long years of struggling between paychecks would be over. No longer would I have to worry about my employer having enough cash in the bank to meet payroll. No longer would I have to prove myself. The company offered me a position that made me feel I was worth something. With added bonuses and benefits, I could rest from financial worry. As my father told me, "You're in the big leagues now, Son!" Yes, it was true, Eric Crane had finally arrived.

And so I had, or so I thought. On the way home from Stapleton Airport, I told Michele all about the fantastic offer. I punctuated my words with a great deal of excitement and flair.

"They made me an offer!" I threw my bag and briefcase in the back seat, hopped in the driver's seat, gave Michele a dutiful husband-to-wife kiss on the cheek and drove off.

"Yeah, and?" she asked with eager anticipation.

"Just like I said, six figures, guaranteed the first year!"

"You're kidding!" Michele was almost screaming with excitement.

"No, really, I got an offer! Can you believe it?" Our enthusiasm was feeding off one another.

"Wow, that's incredible!" Her eyes beamed like a child on Christmas morning.

"He wants me to start July first. What do you think?" I asked as I paid the parking fee and drove out of the airport parking lot.

"What do I think? I think this is an answered prayer, that's what I think." Michele was ecstatic.

I thought, as I drove, "No more lying awake at night wondering if Brian Watkins is going to pay my commissions or not." Every month I had to negotiate how much of my commission he could afford to pay me. That situation would be history, with Systech's six-figure guarantee.

Michele resumed. "Oh Eric, I know this will be good for us. And I know how unhappy you've been working for Brian. Tell me more about the offer. What will you be doing?"

"Systech sells its software to distributors such as Watkins Systems. The company has twelve distributors now, and they want me to build it up to twenty-five over the next two years. The earning potential is double what I earn today at Watkins, and the company is more reliable."

"How much travel is involved?"

"A lot. I'll most likely be traveling every other week, perhaps every week, occasionally." I checked my speed, seventy-five. The speed limit was fifty-five. Better slow down to sixty-five, I thought.

"Well, for a job like that, I guess it's worth it."

"Look at it this way. I'll be making a lot more than I am today, and in a couple of years, I could get a promotion to director of sales for the entire company. And after that, who knows?"

"Do you think we ought to discuss it with the bishop?" Michele was raised a Mormon and always wanted to talk every major decision over with the bishop, a lay minister with no formal ministerial training. In her eyes the bishop held the answers to life's big decisions.

"If you want to. But I've decided I'm taking the job, unless God himself comes down here and tells me otherwise." That was my way of putting my foot down and exercising control. Michele looked away in silence.

I watched the highway markers go by.

She spoke next. "Well, Eric, if you really think so." She hesitated. "I better start packing."

She agreed. When there was a decision to make, it generally went my way. As a convert to Mormonism, I had come to believe in their doctrine of patriarchal order. The husband had authority to make decisions, and the wife should support him. Michele was a dutiful Mormon wife.

"Anyway, the only reason to stay here is the church," I stated in a matter-of-fact tone.

"Suppose you don't get called to the bishopric in Spokane?" Michele knew how much I enjoyed serving.

"If it's meant to be, it's meant to be," I rationalized. "Maybe the people in Spokane need me more than the people in Westminster." My ego spoke vainly.

There was silence. We usually drove in silence. Over the years the marriage had become monotonous, and we didn't talk much. When we did talk, it was about little things like the kids' schoolwork, dance lessons, or a repair on the house.

I like to think while I drive, so I took a few minutes to digest what Michele had said. I was a counselor to the bishop. Michele and I had grown close to the members of our church, who were also our neighbors. We were involved with their births, marriages, illnesses and deaths and whatever else goes on in typical middle-class America.

Since childhood I had dreamed about being a minister. I was in college studying religion when I met Michele and I converted to Mormonism. I gave up my dream of a full-time ministry because Mormons do not have full-time clergy. They simply "called" someone from the congregation to serve as bishop for several years. It was an honor. I was called as a counselor to the bishop. That, too, was considered an honor. Being the bishop's counselor allowed me to realize part of my childhood dream. What if Michele was right and I was not called to serve in Spokane?

The decision to take the job was made; although, deep down inside I felt what I was about to do might be the beginning of the end of a lifestyle I had chosen for my adult life. I disregarded my deep down feelings. They were strangers I did not want to meet. I bottled up my feelings until violent fits of anger forced them out. Like an explosion of fireworks, I had quick bursts of rage that came out of nowhere.

We exited the freeway and began the last few miles to the house. Michele broke the silence. "How did you leave it with Rich?"

"I told him we would talk about it, but that it sounded like we had a deal."

"So what do we do now?" Michele wanted direction.

"We should make arrangements to go up there and look around for a house, I suppose." We agreed to go to Spokane as soon as possible. The kids were just finishing the school year, so we planned the trip to be in two weeks. We made the announcement to her family in person, on our way to Spokane.

My mind returned to the present and I looked over to Vida with a face that wore a question.

"Yes?" Vida said. He must have known I had a question.

"Are we supposed to be talking about this?" I wasn't sure why we were going back in time.

"Is there something else you want to talk about, Eric?"

"No, I don't think so." I was not sure.

"What do you think about your conversation with Michele?"

"You can see it too? I mean, when I think about the past, you can see it?" I wondered.

"I told you we were going to take a trip back. Where I come from we don't have to communicate with words. We also communicate through thoughts."

"You do? How?" He had my attention.

He smiled and touched his heart. "It's all in here."

"So you know what I'm thinking?"

"If you allow me to know." He said kindly.

"And if I don't?" Now I was nervous.

"It's always your choice. You must grant permission for me to know your thoughts." He smiled again and with his hand, gently touched my foot. "You'll see."

The nurse walked in to check on the IV. "You doing okay in here?"

I nodded. I looked at Vida. He grinned from ear to ear. I looked at the nurse, and back to Vida. She walked right by him and didn't see him.

"You can press this button," she showed me the call button on the rail of the bed, "if you need me, okay?"

I nodded again. She walked back by Vida and out the room.

Vida watched her leave and then looked at me. "Told you." Vida sighed.

"That's amazing! Are you real?"

"Ha! I hope so. Here." He pinched my big toe.

"Hey!"

"Is that real?" He lit up.

"I don't understand." It was too much to comprehend.

"You will. Let's go back to where we were, shall we?"

"Okay. I suppose." I shifted the gears of my mind back in time.

"Can you see, Eric, how you were then?"

"What do you mean?"

"How did you treat Michele?"

"Like she was my wife."

"I see. And what does it mean for her to be your wife?"

"That we were married and she," I paused to think. Would he know that I was thinking? I looked up at him. He knew. "That's not fair!"

"You let me." He smiled.

"I suppose I need to be more careful." How did I treat Michele? I wasn't sure I knew what he meant. I treated her okay. I wasn't mean to her. "I treated her fairly, didn't I?"

"Did you? Did you ever ask her how she felt about moving? Did you ever consider her point of view?"

I thought about it for a few minutes. I came up empty.

"No. I can't seem to recall asking her about that." I looked up at the ceiling. I wondered why I never asked her.

"It is important that you consider the other person's feelings. Her feelings are as important as your own." Vida looked me directly in the eye. He was not smiling like he had before. He had a determined look.

He paused briefly, maintained eye contact, and resumed. "Let's go back again. This time to Michele's family in Idaho."

I felt it better not to say anything right away. The scene changed to my in-laws' house in Jefferson County, Idaho. I was the proud son-in-law who had made it big. A Mormon convert who had risen in the church to leadership and authority was being blessed with a great job. As we sat down for dinner Friday evening, I laid it out for them.

"Now that everyone is here, I want to give you some news. The reason Michele and I are taking a trip to Spokane is I am accepting a new job with a company there, Systech Systems. It's a fantastic opportunity, and Michele and I are going to look for a new home."

Her father looked stunned at first. He was a rancher and a farmer all his life, and his face wore the wrinkles and weather-beaten lines of an old cowboy. Each of his expressions had a very distinct look. When his face went from stunned to a big smile, I knew he approved. "Oh Eric, that's wonderful news. So you got a new job offer, a promotion of sorts?"

"Yep. You can sure call it a promotion," I responded proudly.

Michele's mom was timid and polite. "And now you're going to look for a new house? Oh Michele, whatever do you think?" She didn't usually come right out with her own opinions. She was subtler, but everyone who knew her generally understood what she meant. What she was really saying was, "Do you think that's a wise decision to up and move like that? Have you talked it over with your bishop, and have you received his blessing?"

"It's really good for both of us, Mom. We even discussed it with the bishop, and he thinks we should do what's right for us. This seems to be right." Michelle defended our decision.

I hoped my in-laws were realizing they were wrong about me. They had always wanted Michele to marry someone who had grown up in the church and who had the same background, a rancher and a farmer.

I was from the South. I grew up in a fairly "Leave It To Beaver" suburban neighborhood in Richmond, Virginia. My family was strict Southern Baptist, and we attended church every time the doors opened. We had different beliefs and rules than Michele's Mormon family from rural Idaho.

My in-laws were gracious and loving. I tried my best to fit into their world. They must have noticed my awkward attempts, because they always went out of their way to make me feel like I belonged in their family.

My success was welcomed news, especially because Linda, their youngest child, had divorced her husband within the past year. In a small Mormon farming community, divorce was one of the highest disgraces to come upon a family, and my mother in law, a visible person in the community and the church, was shaken as never before. With the announcement of my new job offer, she could divert attention from Linda's divorce to Michele's successful marriage and thus confidently walk among the "elect," as Mormons call themselves. "We are blessed!" would be the unspoken communication to those around her.

After dinner, Michele and I walked through the fields of recently harvested hay. Even though I had hay fever, I enjoyed walking in those green fields of Idaho grain. We walked in silence. Talking is not one of my strengths. I prefer to think.

I had missed the Virginia trees; those lush, enchanted woods where I could hide from the world; the green gardens that appeared even greener after a sizzling summer storm. How I loved to hear the thunder boom like a cannon in battle on those hot Virginia nights. I suppose there was a thunder storm somewhere in Virginia on that June day, but in Idaho, the weather was hot and dry and the landscape had no woods where I could escape. I had to settle for walks in fields of grain.

The one saving grace was the view. In Jefferson County, you can see forever. To the east lie the mighty Teton Mountains. A Frenchman who thought they resembled a woman's breast gave them that name. At almost fourteen thousand feet above sea level, they were visible from the farm. On a clear day, we could see the three giant peaks, even though we were one hundred miles away.

We stopped to look at them. "I could stand here forever and never get tired of this view." I said as I stared.

"Isn't it funny that all those years I lived here, I never really noticed them. I suppose I took this view for granted." Michele fixed her eyes on the same vista.

I thought about the breast. Michele had breastfed our children. I noticed how quickly her breast soothed our babies. The powerful, intimate connection between mother and baby. The world seems to stop when a child nurses a breast. It's as though the child was returning to the warm comfort of the serene womb. I was breastfed. Mom told me. Pity, I don't remember much about it.

When I first saw the Tetons, I felt awe and reverence for their beauty and majesty. I could sit in the shadows of the three peaks and feel serene and calm like the placid Lake Jenny that sat at the base of the Grand Teton and reflected a perfect mirror image of the mountain.

"Spokane has beautiful, clear mountain lakes." I changed the subject and turned to continue the walk. "Perhaps we can find a place to live on one of them."

"Oh, that would be nice, Eric. Do you really think so?"

"Who knows? We can at least look," I had my doubts, but it was worth throwing out for conversation.

"I spoke to Linda today." Michele often made a brief comment like that so that I would follow with a question.

"Oh yeah, what's she up to?" I asked, delivering my part in Michele's innocent game of communication.

"She's so mad at Mom and Dad. She has nothing nice to say about them. She's building this huge wall between herself and them and she can't even see it," Michele's voice crescendoed. "I don't understand what's so bad about Mom and Dad."

Was this my cue? I held back for a moment to see if there was more. "What does she say about them?" I was getting better at the game.

"She talks about how she hates Mom, and how Dad ought to keep out of her business and, ooh, I get mad just thinking about it." Michele walked faster.

"She should consider seeing someone about it." I was trying to solve the problem. Males feel obligated to solve problems and I was a dutiful male, in that sense.

"She won't go near the church. She doesn't like her bishop, she says he's dopey." Michele's rapid walking pace continued.

"I was not referring to the church." Michele's family went to the bishop for counseling on a variety of matters. Health, finances, family matters, spiritual matters, you name it, they talked to the bishop about it. It was unheard of to go for professional help for emotional problems. That would mean that you were really nuts. They did believe the sick and mentally ill should seek professional help; however, they did not consider themselves in that category.

"She's not that messed up, Eric. She just needs time. If we leave her alone, she'll eventually come around."

Michele's words became prophetic. For the next couple of years Linda and her parents spoke little to each other.

"Yeah, sure, whatever. She's a big girl." I commented. My suggestion of seeking help was not well received. Since I had a "my-way-or-the-highway" way of thinking, I had little more to offer in the way of solutions that would be rejected.

Michele changed subjects. "I'm glad we have a good marriage, Eric. Even though it's not perfect, it is good, don't you think." We were still walking side by side. She turned her head, looked at me, and waited for my reply. It was another aspect of her communication game, which called for a quick response from me.

"What is good," I wondered? Was there any marriage I could point to as an example of a "good" marriage? Did I think our marriage was good? Michele had asked me. I had to respond.

"I suppose so," I replied without much energy. I looked away to the evening clouds that had turned red against the deep blue of the western sky. The sun was setting on a sky canvas of blues, oranges, reds, purples and whites as each minute the colors in the clouds changed. The air felt cooler as the sun fell below the horizon.

"You don't sound very convincing." Her worried tone said more than her words.

We convinced each other our marriage was "good" many times in the past, hoping in quiet desperation that if we said the words frequently enough, it would become true. A few months earlier we had received marriage counseling from our bishop, because our then thirteen-year marriage was hopelessly stuck in neutral, and worse, slipping downhill. The outcome of the counseling was the dictum that Michele and I were to continue to be faithful in keeping the commandments and serving the Lord, and blessings would follow. The bishop also told me to be intimate with Michele and gave me a book on intimacy written by a church apostle. The bishop could not tell me how to be intimate; I had to read about it.

We stopped walking and looked at the red and purple dusk sky.

I broke the silence. "I guess there's no such thing as a perfect marriage. The bishop talked about being intimate, and I'm not sure what he means by that. Do you know anyone who has an intimate marriage?" No one had ever before used that word to me as it related to marriage. I tried to read the book, but the content was so foreign to me that I had no concept of what it was trying to say.

"Well, sure. President McKee had a really good marriage," Michelle stated.

President McKee was the head of the Mormon church in the late fifties and early sixties. Church members considered his relationship with his wife a standard for good marriages. Someone had even written a book about it. I never read it. I figured I was married, and that was sufficient.

I asked, "But who else? Who do we know who has a marriage you could call intimate?" Michele and I had sex, sometimes as much as two to three times a month. Wasn't that intimate enough? I had neither the time nor the desire to sit around holding her and talking about how we felt and all that romantic mushy stuff. That behavior was for actors in movies and television. My parents never did that stuff, nor did any other married couple, as far as I was aware of, and once Michele and I got married, who needed it?

Michele tried to think of one married couple we knew who were intimate, who held hands regularly, who laughed and played together, who had excitement in their relationship and who still wanted to date each other for the sake of being together, rather than out of duty or obligation.

"Sally and James," she replied as if she were on a TV quiz show.

"Sally and James? Ha! Their marriage is not intimate. We have sex more often than them, and they never go out together!" I thought sex was synonymous with intimacy. "Come on, don't you know anyone else?" As far back as either of us tried to remember, no one came to mind. We saw couples who experienced intimacy on TV and in movies, but not in real life.

"Well, what difference does it make, anyway? Let's drop it." Michele said disappointedly. She knew intimacy meant more than sex. She must have been frustrated with me in my limited understanding. Our marriage had become an emotional desert.

"Fine." It was okay with me to drop it, as Michele suggested.

We continued our walk in silence. I accepted the fact that our relationship, which for me was based on duty and obligation, was what it was. It would never know tender feelings of love. My reality was obligations, bills, work, children, church and so on and so on, not that other mushy-feeling stuff. Like my dad said to me when Felicia, our first child, was born, "Welcome to the Keep-Your-Nose-To-The-Grindstone Club!"

Dad's comment was reality explained to me. I believed having a family was not something you could feel happy and joyful about. It was serious business, and you better take it seriously. Work hard, live a clean life, and one day you will be a success.

We walked back to her parents' house, went to sleep, and left the next morning for Spokane to look for a new home.

After two days of exhaustive searching, we found our dream house. It was situated on a three-acre spread right outside of Spokane. A clear mountain river ran nearby with "fish me" written all over it.

"I want to explore the area for a while. Do you mind?" I was eager to go see the new surroundings.

"That's fine, Eric. I want to spend some time in the house planning the rooms." Michele had a good sense of where furniture should go. We had an unspoken rule. I took care of the outside, and she took care of the inside.

"I'll be about an hour. Okay?" I was already headed for the woods.
"Sure."

The Spokane forest is rich with an aromatic smell of pine, fir and other native foliage. I found a deer trail and followed it to the river. The river was more like a big creek at the place it flowed by the house. It was no more than a few feet deep and about one hundred feet across. Massive boulders in the middle of the river caused the water to make a loud rippling sound as it moved downstream.

I found a comfortable position on a dried-out tree that had fallen years since. I sat down and looked out over the running river. Overhead I saw an osprey soaring, looking for some lunch. I knew that this was the place for me. I hoped Michele felt the same way.

"Maybe now I can be happy," I thought. I had worked hard, lived a clean life, and I was successful. My marriage and my relationship with the children was the same: distant. I continued to attend church diligently, and yet I was unhappy.

I had taken up fishing, but whenever I returned home from an expedition, I re-entered the dull reality of being a father and a husband. Mr. Provider. I tried golf. It was a waste of perfectly good time that could have otherwise been devoted to work or church, so I felt guilty about being out on the course with so many obligations.

I read almost all of Louis L'Amour's books. They took me back to a simpler time, when men were rough, tough and fast with their guns and fists. They always got the bad guy and won the heart of a beautiful woman.

I felt no joy and no excitement about life. I merely kept on going, accepting my world for what it was: cold, gray steel.

"Maybe," I thought, "things will be different when the children are grown and on their own." I decided to stick it out until that future day. Like a prisoner who quietly serves his sentence, I waited for the day of liberation from my boring life. The day would eventually arrive when I could walk out the door of my marriage with no more obligations. I dreamt of being a free man.

I thought back to a day in Westminster, during my daily commute from work, how desperate and hopeless I felt about life. "Why don't you get divorced and leave?" I asked myself.

"Because, it would be too hard on the children," I answered. I often thought about escaping the marriage but I decided I did not want my children to suffer the pain that comes from divorce. I had gone through a great deal of pain when my parents divorced. I preferred to continue in the marriage than to create suffering for my children.

"Besides," my thinking continued, "I can't afford to provide for two households." I felt trapped. So, in my mind, I banished the thought of leaving to a remote chamber somewhere in the deep, dark, cold caverns of my being and went on with life, gritting my teeth, smiling politely to everyone, while silently cursing within.

From day one of our relationship, Michele and I did not communicate well. We argued and fought frequently. We could not discuss anything, whether it be of significance or not, without her getting emotional and my getting angry. Our communication, if you could call it that, was a constant battle. When we weren't on the offense hurling rockets and spears, we were both on the defense, trying to prove our individual viewpoints.

We did not listen to what the other was trying to say. I never opened up or allowed her to see inside me. I did not want her to see the real me. I had closed myself and built an impenetrable fortress around my heart. No one was allowed inside: not my wife, my children, my family of origin nor my friends. A sick part of me viewed them as the enemy. I felt like a victim. Under the circumstances, our marriage had no chance of growing and very little hope for survival.

Despite the lack of intimacy in our relationship, we kept on. I was not going to be a "non-hacker!" I was going to "endure to the end." If I could fix problems at work and at church, certainly I could do the same at home.

A voice brought me back to the present. "Mr. Crane? Here's your dinner." Time had passed quickly. The hospital volunteer brought lunch into my room. Turkey, corn and peas, red gelatin and two percent milk. I offered some to Vida.

"No, thanks." He waved his hands as if to stop a truck.

"They really know how to spoil a guy in here." I said sarcastically and stirred the peas. I decided to eat the meal anyway, because I was hungry.

"Eric, why didn't you allow Michele to see inside you?"

I put down my fork, looked at Vida and then out the window. I had no answer, no clue, no defense. It never crossed my mind before now. "Why?" Vida had asked. My mind created a picture of a restaurant entry door. In the middle was a black sign with neon red letters, "Closed." I looked at Vida who was still looking at me. "I was closed?"

"That's right, Eric, and you still are, too. I have come to help you open up to your True Self."

"My true self?" Once more, I was lost. I pushed the supper tray away and pushed back down into the bed. My back was aching and my legs needed to stretch. I would learn the answer to my question over the next few days.

– *Two* –

"HAVE YOU EVER MET A WOMAN WHO MADE YOUR GROIN MOVE THE moment you laid eyes on her? Did your heart beat fast and your mouth salivate?" Vida asked with a serious look on his face.

"Sure." I nodded. I knew exactly what he meant. "Twice."

"Tell me." Vida smiled, anticipating a good story.

I went back to the first morning of my new job at Systech. I wore my navy blue pinstriped Hart, Shafner & Marx suit, and my corporate smile was working double-time. Martha, my administrator, was introducing me to the other employees, when I first noticed the most beautiful eyes I had ever seen on a woman. The twinkle in these green eyes told me they were different from all the other eyes I had ever seen. Due to my heavy travel schedule I must have seen thousands of eyes in airports, restaurants and office buildings, but the electricity in these eyes told me they were different.

Without saying a word, for an instant, a brief, almost imperceptible moment of eternity, communication flashed between our eyes. I stopped listening to Martha. Time stood still, and although life around me continued, I no longer heard what was being said; I no longer played in the script. I stood frozen by feelings and primal urges. These eyes held an enchanted spell that overpowered me. The woman behind these eyes was Donna.

Over time, I saw her again, and whenever I did, our eyes formed a cosmic connection. Our first spoken words were the usual, courteous "hello's," but in my heart I knew, we were able to communicate beyond words as if by some strange, undefined mystical force. Whenever we were about to be in the presence of one another, we sensed it beforehand.

After a few months, Donna and I began to say more than the usual "How are you/I'm fine..." to each other. There were times we met in the employee lunchroom and talked. The subjects varied from life, religion, children, relationships and work. She was divorced with a four-year-old son. I told her all about my children. Like me, Donna had earned her way through college. I liked her independence and intelligence, that was such a contrast to some women I knew who were dependent upon their husbands or their children for a sense of self. Donna was alluring. I eagerly looked forward to our conversations.

I looked at Vida, thinking I should stop.

"You felt something when you looked at her?" he asked.

"Sure, I felt something." I said, irritated by his seemingly obvious question.

"What?" He proceeded to ask despite my irritation.

I paused for a moment to get over my irritation. "I liked her. I felt attracted to her."

"When I asked if you had ever felt your groin move when you first met a woman, you answered 'twice'. Donna was the first. Who was second?" Vida asked.

"Sonnie." I looked out the window as I thought about her. At a little over five-feet-six, Sonnie was a sight. Her curvy body turned me on instantly. She had blue and gray eyes and long silky smooth blonde hair.

"Ah, Sonnie." Vida smiled like a child.

There was a brief moment of silence, followed by my next remark.

"Sonnie still makes me feel that way."

"And what if Donna walked into your room right now. How would you feel about that?"

"How would I feel?" Suppose she would walk in here after all those years? Would I feel the same way I did when we first met? Would I want her, as I did back then? I looked at Vida. Oh my God, did he know what I was thinking? He looked right at me. I wondered, what he thought? Was he searching for some sort of an answer? I looked away.

Okay, I had an affair with Donna. It was brief, but it happened, and it was intense. I cut it off after I moved to Atlanta and met Sonnie. I thought, "What would happen if she suddenly walked through the hospital doors and into my room?"

"I would be nervous." I blurted out loud.

"Why is that, Eric?" Vida leaned toward me.

"Because I'm not sure how I might react to seeing her. Suppose the attraction was the same?" I felt that if I still had feelings toward Donna, I would betray Sonnie by having such feelings.

"Would it surprise you to still be attracted to Donna?" Vida stood and walked toward the door.

"Where are you going?" I was afraid he was leaving. I felt panicked and desperately wanted an answer to his question.

"Nowhere. Just stretching." He yawned as he stretched and returned to the chair.

"Let's go back there, Eric. Back to Spokane. Back to the affair. Breathe slowly, relax, breathe, easy, back, back, back."

A group of us from Systech went out one evening after work to celebrate the holidays. It was Christmas time, and everyone was in a festive mood, except me. I didn't much care for Christmas. Christmas was merely another excuse to spend money, that I never seemed to have, for presents for people I wouldn't normally buy presents for. I often thought we should go to the bank, put a few thousand dollars into a fund that everyone could access, take out what they needed, and that would be the end of it.

I decided to go out with the office group that evening because Donna was going.

We went to Lucky's Tavern, a downtown bar, and ordered pizzas and pitchers of beer. The fourteen of us definitely brought Lucky's to life that night. Donna and I sat across from each other.

The modest bar had plain wooden tables left over from the forties. Years of drinks had been poured at our table. Soldiers coming home from some distant war far across the Pacific. Politicians and bankers talked about everything and nothing while no one really listened. The walls had heard it all. Lucky's was packed. Everyone crowded at the bar to watch the TV that hung up on the wall at the end of the bar. The first TV had been replaced somewhere in time with a color model that now flickered and needed repair. The locals had come to watch the first man walk on the moon, over draft beer and cheap scotch. The Vietnam war began in black and white and ended in color. Nixon resigned and John Lennon was assassinated, and was watched on the TV at Lucky's.

The talk at the table that cold December night was the usual work-related conversation. We talked about office politics, plans for the holidays, Santa's goodies for the children and our solutions to the federal deficit. A few hours later and a dozen of downed pitchers of beer, our group left for home.

I walked Donna to her car because it was dark and the parking lot was remote, and I didn't want her to walk alone. When we said good-bye that night, we touched hands, for a nano-second, but it was a touch, nonetheless. It was that touch that sent off a fire alarm inside my body. I felt something shake in the inner sanctum of my soul. What it was, I did not know. I only knew that it made me quiver, and I wanted to find out what it was, and quickly.

The next day was Saturday. I went to the office with an obsession to find Donna's phone number and address. I felt I had to talk to her. I had a burning desire to know if what I felt was something she felt too, or if it was some ridiculous childish feeling I was feeling alone.

I quickly looked through all of my desk drawers for the employee directory. The last drawer was the winner. Now let's see, D-; Da-; Dabney; Dahle; Davis; Dawson, Donna ... one thirty-three Fourth Street. I nervously picked up the phone receiver and dialed her number. The line was busy. I called again, same result. After several failed attempts, I left and drove like a crazy man to her small house in an older part of town. The streets were packed with day-old snow and ice, but I drove carelessly like it was a sunny day in June. I could see through the beveled leaded glass windows on the side of her oak front door that Donna was still on the phone. With apprehension I rang her doorbell.

She looked at the door to see who it was. I guess she was not expecting company, because the surprised look on her face seemed to say "Oh my God!" She obviously had not been expecting me, of all people. She hung up the telephone and came over and opened the door.

"Hello." I at least managed to blurt that much out. I felt awkward.

"Eric, what are you doing here?" She may have been surprised to see me, but her face had one of those "I'm-so-glad-to-see-you" smiles.

"Well, I uh, uh, can I come in?" It was an extremely cold day and my curiosity to know what was going on in her head boiled inside me. I had a little boy feeling inside, like when you see a girl you really like and you lose all your macho-ness and melt to mush with no brains.

"Sure, come on in! Want some hot tea?"

"That would be great." I stood in the living room self-consciously looking around as she walked to the kitchen.

"Make yourself at home!" she yelled over her shoulder "I was just cleaning the place up and got tied up on the phone."

I looked around the front room. A Raphael angel print hung over the mantel of the fireplace. On the wall opposite was an Ansel Adams black-and-white poster print of the Tetons. On the hardwood floors were accent rugs, and the couch was an older, overstuffed model, taupe colored, from the fifties.

"What am I doing?" I thought. "This is strange. I should leave. She's going to think I'm nuts." I was so nervous I could not think.

"Here, its chamomile," she said as she entered the room and handed me a cup. "Have a seat." She motioned to the couch and took her seat in an old rose-colored chair across from me. The expression on her face told me she was still trying to figure out why I was there.

"Thanks." I grabbed the tea and sat down, all in one quick move.

"So what brings you here?"

"I'm not sure," I lied. "Well, uh, I really don't know how to say it, but something weird happened to me last night when we were saying good-bye and our hands touched."

She nodded as if she knew exactly what I was talking about as she sipped her tea. She looked at me with her seductive eyes, looked down and then looked at me again. "Yes." It was a whisper, but she said it and I heard it.

I took a deep breath. "Well, this may sound crazy, I mean, I'm a married man with children, and this isn't supposed to happen to me, but something happened and I can't explain it, and it felt good, and," I was rambling. "Well, I just needed to know if you felt it too." I wasn't sure where I was going with that, it came out raw and unedited.

"Yes, I felt it too, and I've thought about it, all night. I didn't know what to do about it either."

I became silent and felt uncomfortable. I looked at her, then down at the floor and over to the window. I spoke next. "Well, I guess we should do nothing. I guess we should just forget it and go on like nothing happened because I can't - "

Donna interrupted. "I understand."

"I mean nothing like this has happened before." I pleaded.

"It's all right, Eric." She sensed my awkwardness.

"Well," Why did everything start out with "well" I felt like Ronald Reagan. "I suppose I should leave."

"Okay."

I handed her my cup, and we walked toward the door.

"Donna, before I go - I mean – well, (oh brother! Come-on Crane, you can do better than this!) may I give you a hug?"

It seemed as though time stopped. I felt like a child waiting while his father reviews his report card, and wonders if he's going to notice the F's and D's. A few seconds can feel like a few hours during such a review.

In a heartbeat, we stood, took a couple of steps toward each other and embraced. The passionate hug was filled with energy like I had not experienced before. I closed my eyes and let go of a tremendous amount of tension from deep inside and then I felt energy come from her. I smelled her hair, noticed her breasts against my chest, felt her stomach touch mine and our hips fit together like magnets. Her embrace became tighter. My penis swelled with desire. I was losing control and had to stop. I abruptly pushed away.

"Good-bye, Donna." I said quickly. I had to leave. The temptation to stay was almost overpowering. I moved closer to the door and reached for the knob.

"Good-bye, Eric." She said quietly. With mixed emotions, I walked out. I got in the car and drove away, not straight home, just somewhere, anywhere. I felt something in my gut rumble. It ran up to my chest as it thumped harder and harder, like the big bass drum in a college marching band. Then my throat trembled and my eyes quivered as they filled with - tears? I think I was feeling passion like I had only felt in my dreams. I cried. Soft at first, then harder, as my emotions began to surface.

As I sat in my hospital bed, fresh with the emotion of the event, I felt a tear come from my right eye first, then my left. Vida looked at me empathetically.

"That's how it started," I said in a soft tone. I wasn't sure if I should continue, so I looked at Vida for direction.

"You were thinking about a dream. Tell me about it," he said.

"There were several dreams. In one of them I dreamt I was with a woman. I felt connected to her. There was a sense of completeness with her that felt good to me. She was a beautiful woman, much different from Michele. She was shorter and had long, shiny blonde hair and a physique you saw in magazines." I looked up at the ceiling as I recalled the dream.

"Her skin was baby soft, and her perfume sent my hormones into the red zone. We had an energy between us that felt liberating and exhilarating. I have not experienced a feeling like that in my marriage to Michele, although from my dream I knew I wanted it and had sorely missed it when I woke up. I wondered if I would ever experience the feeling of passion I felt in the dream in my real life." I looked at Vida, who encouraged me to continue by gesturing with his hand.

"The dreams didn't always contain sex. A familiar bond connected us. I felt safe, as if I had returned to a home I had left long before. Was that the feeling a child has when nursing from the breast?" I looked at Vida. He met my eyes and smiled as if he understood what I felt. I continued.

"I never wanted those dreams to end. When I woke up, I sank deep into despair, because that feeling of completeness vanished, and I no longer felt the connection. Although I never told Michele, she must've suspected something had happened, because after a dream like that I immediately got out of bed and was distant emotionally. In fact, I secretly resented her for not being the goddess in my dreams."

I reached for the control on the hospital bed and raised my head.

"I resigned myself to the fact that the feelings I had in my dreams weren't possible to achieve in my life. They could only occur in my dreams with a mystery woman. I didn't want to accept that, but felt as though I had no choice. For some reason, I felt I didn't deserve love like that. I thought I had to accomplish more, to gain more power and more money, to be worthy of such a love.

"Crazy, huh?" I looked at Vida for some reassurance.

"Eric, what are you looking for?"

"Looking for?" I was surprised by his question. "I'm not sure I know what you mean."

"Your soul directed you to find something through your dreams. What is it?" Vida inquired.

"You mean as it relates to Donna?"

He shrugged his shoulders as if to say "could be," and waited for me to answer.

"I dreamt about having passionate feelings with a woman. I was connected to the woman in a way that felt like she was a part of me."

Vida uncrossed his legs and leaned forward. "A part of you. What part of you?"

I had not considered what part of me. Was there only a part of me that felt connected in my dream, or was it all of me?

"There was a connection Vida, and it made me feel complete. I can't say it was this part of me or that part of me. The feeling was blissful. I could let go of my energy and let it flow from me to her, without any effort. It flowed freely."

"Who is the woman in your dreams?" Vida leaned forward.

Silence. I pondered. Was the woman in my dreams Donna? My mother? Michele?

"Eric, dreams often reveal to us certain aspects of ourselves. Who is the woman?"

"Me?" I took his clue and guessed.

Vida leaned back in his chair and nodded affirmatively.

"Me? How does she represent me?" Once more, I was lost.

"There are two basic energies in all of us. One is masculine and the other is feminine. This does not mean masculine and feminine as in gender or sexuality. It is masculine and feminine in forms of energy. Like Ying and Yang, there must be a balance of masculine and feminine energy in all humans."

"Vida, I don't get this." I said in a confused tone.

"Your dream is telling you, in part, to connect to the feminine aspect of your self. The feminine is the intuitive, loving nature of your being. At a soul level you are a combination of masculine and feminine energy. In your human incarnation, your personality, Eric, is primarily composed of masculine energy, which is that energy used for logical and linear thinking. It is associated primarily with science. Feminine energy is intuitive and synchronistic. It is associated primarily with spirit." Vida stood and walked over to the window.

"The universe is full of masculine and feminine energy. Think of Mars, the warrior and Venus, the lover as archetypes of masculine and feminine energy. Consider the Sun as the powerful masculine energy of generating light, and the Moon as the feminine energy that receives and reflects the Sun's light. And yet, both are part of the same solar system, of the same Universe." He turned to look at me.

"As a male you are expected to be masculine as a person. Society teaches you to act male-like, to think logically and to accept what is truth by that which can be measured and explained through science. However; in teaching you this, you ignored your feminine energy and thus you are so out of touch with your spiritual self, it is foreign to you."

"How do the feelings of passion, connection and completion relate to what you just described, Vida?" I could not make the association.

"When you balance the feminine and masculine energies within, you will feel complete." He smiled a knowing smile. "We will come back to this later, Eric. There is another dimension to explore regarding the dream."

"And that is?" I was not sure where this discussion was going.

"Your marriage to Michele lacked the intimacy and spontaneity of the feminine energy. When you were with Donna you allowed yourself to experience these energies of a relationship. Your marriage was built primarily upon masculine principles of duty, obligation and therefore it contained a very masculine energy. It is little wonder you awoke from your dreams and felt distant to Michele. You left the bliss of the feminine energy in your dream to the coolness of the masculine energy in your mortality."

"You cannot have an intimate marriage if you do not balance the masculine and feminine energies within yourself and then bring this balance into your marriage. You cannot enter into a marriage needing to find what you do not have as an individual and expect the marriage to supply it.

"Your marriage should be built on what you can offer it, not what you need from it. You cannot feel completion from a marriage if you do not have completion within yourself."

I had to take a moment to digest what Vida had spoken. Caught up in my thoughts, I did not notice him move to the door.

"I will leave you with these concepts, Eric. Continue to ponder them." He turned to leave.

Startled by his statement, I asked, "When will you return?" I felt like he may be deserting me and I wanted him to stay.

"Soon." His look was reassuring. He walked toward the door and vanished.

The phone rang. "Hello?"

"Hi, Eric, how are you feeling?" It was my older sister Carla, the only family member I had in Atlanta.

"Much better, thanks. How about you?" I was glad to hear her voice.

"Oh, just the usual. I called because I just read something and I thought of you." Carla had a cheery tone.

"Thanks." I said with appreciation for her thoughtfulness.

"Have you been able to rest?"

"That's about all I do here. Sleep and lie around daydreaming." I laughed as I spoke.

"Well, good. You need a lot of rest, Eric. You've been pushing yourself very hard trying to do too much. You need to slow down some, maybe a lot." Carla was like a second mother to me and was concerned about my welfare.

I laughed, not at her question, but at her motherly manner. "Yeah, maybe I do."

"No, I'm serious, you can only do so much, and you've been trying to do it all. Anyway, here's what I read. Are you ready?"

"Sure." I was glad to know she cared enough to actually find something to read to me.

" 'Be still and know that I am God.' "

I said nothing. It struck a chord within and I could not speak. Unlike what had happened a couple of days ago, this was not a physical inability to speak, rather it was an emotional inability to find words that expressed the profoundness of what Carla had just read. A lump formed in my throat.

"Eric, are you still there?"

"Yes." My voice was barely audible.

"Well, what do you think?"

"I think you hit the nail right on the head. That's exactly where I am. I have been listening to God's messengers for the past couple of days. What you just read confirms that what is happening is by God's direction."

"What messengers?" Carla was highly intrigued, so I explained the events since the paramedics picked me up.

"Wow. That's amazing, Eric. I don't quite know what to say. What's it like to have celestial visitors?"

"It's like being in the presence of pure peace. They know what's going on inside of you, and yet they accept you completely as you are and love you unconditionally."

"That must be awesome." Carla replied.

"It's more than that, Carla. It's beyond words. I have never experienced unconditional love like this. It's scary to spill my guts out to these beings, yet it's comforting at the same time. They understand me and don't judge me."

I could hear Carla's loud doorbell in the background.

"Oh no," Carla blurted out. "Eric, someone's at the front door. I want to hear more about this. I'll call again tomorrow, if that's okay?"

"Sure, that will be fine. Thanks for your comforting words."

"You're welcome. Good-bye, Eric."

"Good-bye, Carla."

I hung up the phone and thought about what Carla had read. I was definitely still here in the hospital. But what about God? I was angry with God, and I did not want to think about Him. I felt I had devoted my life to a traffic cop in the sky who waited for me to make a mistake, so it could be recorded for the judgment day.

"Abliel, are you there?" I was feeling angry with God, which in turn created a sense of guilt. I needed to talk.

"I am always here, Eric." Abliel replied lovingly.

"What about God? What do I do about God?"

"God loves you, Eric, just as you are. He can only reveal Himself to you to the extent you have allowed. Your years of religious training have led you to define your 'God' erroneously. Your interpretation of God is not the God of the universe, as we know him. In time, you will begin to comprehend who God truly is. For now, just listen to Vida and me, and we will help you find your way."

"My way?" I did not understand that last remark.

"Rest, Eric. Don't try to figure everything out all at once. You are where you are for a reason. Continue with your current direction and more will be revealed to you over time." Abliel's tone was always loving and gentle.

I thought, "He said to continue with my current direction." Vida and I had been looking retrospectively at my life. He led me to a discussion about God's nature, which put me in touch with my anger with God. I thought about it and realized that although I had been an active member of the Mormon Church and done exactly what was prescribed as a set of behaviors by the Church, I felt no peace in my life. I had achieved financial success in the business world, yet I felt hollow and wanted more. I was married and had beautiful loving children, yet there was no lasting joy in my life. But the more I thought of God, the angrier I became. It was then that Vida reappeared.

"Abliel tells me you have some questions about God?" Vida walked toward me.

I shared my current thoughts about being angry at God with him and exclaimed, "I'm really angry! I feel like the Church misled me about how to find happiness. I feel betrayed and disappointed too."

Vida replied in a calm voice, "The problem is not about who God is, but rather, your perception of God. One of the Ten Commandments says not to make graven images, which is what you have done, Eric. It's your image of God, and your image of others, that is the problem."

"My image of others?" I was confused.

"You created an image of what your wife should be, then set out to find someone to fit your image. Fitting into your image of a wife is an impossible task for anyone to accomplish, yet you expected Michele to do just that."

What was the image of a wife I had created? She had to be someone who was there when I needed her. She had to know how to cook, to keep a clean house, to bear and to raise my children. I suddenly realized there was no mention of a lover and a friend in my image of a wife. I was married to a domestic worker. How could I be intimate with a domestic worker? Michele was a victim of my distorted image of a wife. I felt hopeless.

"I see what you mean," I confided to Vida in a solemn tone. "There was no way the marriage could work under those circumstances." I began to understand.

"Let's go back in time to Spokane. Tell me about your life," Vida directed as he sat in the chair by my bed.

I went back in my mind to Systech and described the scene to Vida. "At the time I was flying across the country on business every other week. When I was home, I was either reading my Louis L'Amour books, watching TV or attending church. I spent little time with my children. Occasionally I took Michael fishing. Michele and I made no time for one another except an occasional double-date with friends from church or when we went to a church-related function we felt obligated to attend.

"I was happy to be out of town. Although I missed my children, I stayed on the road for a week, sometimes two, at a time. The thrill of a business deal was better for me than the routine of domestic life. I felt euphoric when I closed deals. The friendly skies and the business world were places where I was comfortable. Home became a place where I changed gears, changed clothes and changed roles. It was not a fun place for me to be.

"My sense of accomplishment about closing sales made me feel confident about what I was doing at work. However, deep inside, laid dormant anger and rage that would awaken when I felt desperate. I couldn't predict when those desperate feelings would crop up. I had no conscious awareness of my anger. Rage was a slumbering giant on the floor of the ocean in my mind. As long as everything went according to my plan I had no problem. But as soon as things did not go my way, I exploded with rage, albeit briefly. I never physically hit Michele. I did spank the children and, when I was enraged, I would hit them harder than necessary. After the rage attack was over, I retreated into my church work or television or business matters. Once, I sent my fist through a wall, a stupid thing in retrospect, I know." I looked at Vida with shame.

He sensed my feelings. "It's okay, Eric. Please continue."

"The rage was a powerful foe. It erupted at unpredictable times as if a team of terrorists took over my emotions and I lost my ability to be reasonable. At times my rage was like a fire that swept through the dry timbers of my heart and I would lash out uncontrollably to those I wanted to love, but whom I was incapable of loving."

Vida intervened, "You will learn to love them unconditionally, Eric. I will show you how." Vida wore a hopeful expression. "You cannot love others any more than you love yourself. Self-love is the garden wherein love for others can grow. You had an image of a God that only loved you if you were doing what you thought was right. You felt unworthy of his love. That is conditional love and God is incapable of loving with conditions.

"You cannot love yourself unconditionally and at the same time have an image of a god that loves you conditionally. You must first change your image of God to a god of unconditional Love who accepts you as you are at this moment. You must get rid of your old image of God and let Him create a new image within you."

"How will God do that?" I asked. If there was something I could do to make the change occur, I wanted to know it.

"You can begin by affirming God's true nature to yourself each night as you drift to sleep. Say, *My God is a god of unconditional love who accepts me completely as I am today.* Repeat this over and over again until you fall asleep each evening."

"That's it?" It sounded too easy.

"That is the initial step. I will have you do more as you are ready. I must go now." Vida stood up and prepared to leave.

"Okay," I said. "I will start tonight. Thanks, Vida."

"With pleasure." He gave me a slight salute and departed.

That night I dreamt about a young boy who had bright sunshine-yellow hair and beautiful brown sparkling eyes. He was singing a song with a pleasing melody. He sang with clear perfect notes. His neck was in a noose, and I was about to execute him, but his eyes looked so sad and tender that I had to stop. I stopped and listened to his beautiful song and as I looked at him, I noticed tears trickling from his sad eyes.

Then I awoke. In horror and panic, I lay in bed recounting the dream. The child was intimately familiar. I knew him and yet I was trying to kill him. Why?

I recalled a similar dream from the past wherein I heard a male child's voice but could not see him. I listened and the sound was coming from the lower kitchen cabinets. As I opened the cabinet door, I saw a little boy tucked away inside. Fear of dying was inscribed in his cherubic face. I could have helped him out, but instead, for some strange reason, I filled the cabinet with water to silence him. His sad eyes and the anguish of his face seemed to plea for help. Before I drowned him, I awoke.

I recalled in yet another dream, a little boy did something wrong, something quite innocent, but it enraged me and I severely beat the child with a leather strap to a point of near death. As in other dreams, I awoke before his death occurred, panic stricken and my heart racing.

The horror I felt after awakening from these dreams was so terrifying that I felt I had actually murdered the child. I awoke trembling and sweating, as if I had seen a monster. I concluded that the dreams were telling me that something was profoundly wrong in my life, and that if I did not correct it, I would take out my anger and rage on my children in the form of severe punishment.

I wondered what Vida would say about my dreams.

– *Three* –

"WHAT WOULD YOU LIKE ME TO SAY?" VIDA HAD RETURNED DURING the remembrance of my dreams.

I felt like being sarcastic. "Whatever happened to hello?"

"Sorry, Eric. I forgot you do things differently here. I had no intention of being rude," he said, sincerely.

"That's okay." How could I be upset with him? After all, he is my Teacher. "So, what do you think about my dreams?"

He moved over to the chair, sat down and leaned back, put his hands behind his head and crossed his legs.

"Unfortunate." He looked up at the ceiling and then at me. "What's happened to you that makes you feel so sad?"

I had no answer to give him.

"Tell me about yourself, Eric. Let's start with your career. You said you wanted to be a minister, but that when you joined the Mormon Church, you gave up that dream. How did the change in your plans occur?" Vida put his hands on his lap as he asked that question.

"I was attending college studying for the ministry when I met Michele. We worked together one summer at a hotel in the Grand Teton National Park. While I was there, I converted to the Mormon religion and with remorse gave up my dream.

"When summer was over, I took a job as an insurance salesman. That was the start of my business life, and I immediately shifted gears from a career in the ministry to one in the business world. Inwardly I resented giving up my dream, but I rationalized my decision by accepting the Mormon faith as Truth."

I looked at Vida who mumbled something as he shook his head. "That's tragic." He commented.

"Well, I agree, now." I paused and felt there was no need to linger on that thought, so I continued.

"I set a goal to earn one hundred thousand dollars a year before I reached age thirty. For years, I heard the mighty mouths of motivation preach the gospel of goals to hungry and ambitious sales representatives like me.

"Goals are the golden keys to financial success, and, they told me, all I needed to be rich, were goals. So I set my financial goal to earn one hundred thousand dollars, broke it into smaller increments of eighty-five hundred dollars a month or four hundred and fifty dollars a day. I figured out how many sales I would need to accomplish my financial feat, over a twelve-month period. I then translated that number into how many presentations and how many telephone calls I had to make a day. I realized my time was worth at least fifty dollars an hour, or more, and every time I felt like I wasted fifteen minutes I felt I had wasted about fifteen dollars. Needless to say I was obsessed with making this goal a reality. Nothing could keep me from attaining my goal, including my family, after all, I was doing it for them."

I paused briefly and contemplated what I had said as I stared at the sky through my window. Then I turned back to Vida who was listening to me intently.

"I thought attaining my financial goal would make me a success, and that success meant joy, happiness and peace of mind. At age thirty-four, I finally reached my goal. Although I was off by four years, I had achieved it - the financial part, that is.

"Interestingly enough, even though I could pay the bills and have extra cash for other things, I felt the same inside. Something kept nagging at me, a feeling of unrest and uneasiness. Michele and I were not getting closer; I still had little patience for my children; and I was having those haunting dreams about the desperate little boy."

"You were making money, but you felt something was missing?" Vida wanted to confirm my statement.

"Exactly. I mean, if money and accomplishments weren't enough to make me feel good and successful, then what could possibly make me feel that way? I had listened to a voice in my head tell me to drive, drive, drive and don't let anything get in my way of achieving my goal, because attaining my goal would make me feel successful. Well, I reached my financial pinnacle, and I felt the same. Empty."

Vida massaged the inside corners of his eyes, next to his nose. "How truly sad." His tone was sincere.

"Odd, isn't it?" I snickered. "I had achieved my monetary goal, then wondered why success felt so hollow. Shouldn't I feel happy? After all, I achieved my goal!"

Vida looked at me and said, "Think about the men you know. Who among them are the way you think you should feel?"

I thought for a moment. How many men, that I know personally, actually lived life with a sense of lasting joy? "I don't know, right off the bat. I've met some men who seem to have joy."

"Can you give me an example?" Vida asked affably.

"Rich Hutchinson." Rich was the only one I could come up with at that moment.

"And Rich is successful and happy and everything you feel you should be?"

"Well, yeah, I guess you could say that." I felt challenged by Vida's questions.

"Interesting." Vida mumbled, then he spoke up. "Why can you only come up with one name?"

"I know a lot of successful guys, but I don't know how many of them have joy or happiness. Men don't talk about how they feel with one another. Anyway, what's your point?" I wanted to know where this was going.

"Many men, like you, believe they need to accomplish goals and collect trophies and awards to feel they have worth rather than feeling good for who they are."

"That's it? That's your explanation of why I don't feel joy from achieving my goals?" I was puzzled.

"Men who feel this way have no Self." Vida replied as he crossed his legs.

"No self?" Now I was really puzzled.

"No Self. Men who feel like something is missing, who find themselves in your state of mind have no Self."

I was lost. "Sorry, but I don't follow you."

"The reason these men don't feel more joy in their lives is, their self identity is defined through external pursuits." Vida was trying his best to help me understand, but I still did not get what he was saying.

"No self?" I asked. "What the heck does that mean." I was confused about the word "self".

Vida changed positions. "Let's talk about men in general, shall we?"

"Please. I'm not understanding you, Vida."

He cleared his throat and spoke, "Men are taught that success comes from setting and attaining financial, personal and career goals, to name a few. They often attend numerous sales-training and goal-setting seminars, read many books and listen to motivational tapes to learn better methods to reach their goals. When they achieve their goal, they are 'successful' and rightly so, because their goal is attained. But tell me, Eric, why is the happiness of reaching a goal only temporary?"

I shrugged my shoulders to indicate my lack of an answer.

"Men are taught to achieve and to provide financially, to be viewed as a success in life. They define success by the receipt of a reward from attainment of their goal. These men believe the reward brings happiness. When the feeling of happiness leaves, these same men think they have to set another goal and begin the cycle again.

He continued his explanation, "It is foreign for these men to feel joyful about who they are as a human being. They become a human doing. To feel of worth, they think they have to do something or have a title or status that proves they are successful." Vida stood up and walked to the window.

"Accomplishments are what these men use to define who they are. Goals become like an addictive drug to them. They become obsessed to do more, never satisfied with the results, no matter how successful they might appear. The more men accomplish and succeed, the more they feel they must accomplish and succeed." He looked out the window as he spoke. "The cycle is never-ending and can lead these men to an early heart attack, stroke or suicide. They feel they can never do enough, because more is expected. Society expects the vice-president to become the president and the president to become the CEO and the CEO to become the Chairman of the Board. Then these men, who have been granted an illusion of power by a lifeless corporation, crawl away to retirement and die, because they have no title to tell them how important they are. They have no Self, or identity, outside of their former business title." When Vida finished, he returned to his chair.

"Why do I need to accomplish something to feel a good sense of self?" I took one of my pillows from behind my back, fluffed it and returned it. I knew we were onto something important and I wanted to savor every word.

Vida paused and looked at me. "Remember when you were little and you took your toys apart as soon as you got them?"

"Yes," I replied, astonished that he could know so much.

"As a boy, you wanted to understand the true working of things, so you dismantled your toys to see how they worked." He moved to the edge of the chair. "You still want to know how it all works, don't you, Eric?" He asked with a fatherly smile. I nodded in agreement.

He continued to explain, "When you discovered you were a unique being, rather than part of your mother, you went through a process of adjustment. You left the intimacy of her breast and developed your own identity. Eventually you discovered the gender difference between you and your mother. This discovery caused you emotional trauma because there was a time, when as an infant, you thought you and your mother were the same being. Now, not only were you a different being, you were male and she was female." Vida stood and kept speaking.

"You needed to heal that trauma and define your identity, or your Self, but you were not equipped to do so at that young age. Your socialization process began and through the process, you developed your incorrect sense of Self." Vida moved closer to me and spoke again.

"From day one, you were taught and expected to be different from your sisters. You wore blue clothes, and they wore pink. You had mechanical, lifeless toys like automobiles, while your sisters had life-like dolls. You built streets, buildings and cities with your trucks, cars and construction equipment while your sisters played house with their dolls and toy furniture. You played war with guns and helmets, while your sisters played dress-up with costumes and baby dolls. You learned rough, macho sports and were taught it is sissy to cry, or, to play with dolls, or, to play jump rope."

I leaned up and asked, "So what's the point?"

"The point is, you were being taught how to be a male by your parent's definition, who were taught by their parents, who were taught by their parents and so it goes. Each generation through time has defined what it means to be a male or a female. The role of being male varies by the society in which you are born. Obviously you, Eric, were born into an American Judeo-Christian society and therefore were socialized by that society's standards. Your society has wrongly defined a male's role."

"And that is?" I asked.

"The male's role from the ancient hunting and gathering societies until recently has been to provide leadership in the home, in the community, in business and government and in religion and education." Vida walked toward the window.

"You said 'until recently', what's changed?"

He turned to me. "Consciousness."

"What is consciousness and what does it have to do with a sense of self?" I inquired.

"Consciousness is awareness. As mankind grows in awareness, the society as a whole evolves into a new era. From the hunting and gathering societies to the industrial age to the new age that is upon you, mankind has evolved in consciousness. This has allowed new breakthroughs and discoveries to enable mankind to learn even more. As your society becomes enlightened, you are able to better understand who you truly are as individuals. Recently, your society's awareness of what it means to be a male has evolved so that the macho-male myth of previous generations can be corrected." Vida moved closer to the bed.

"This process of growth and enlightenment must take place on a personal level before it can occur on the societal level. That is why you are in this hospital. You are beginning to grow in awareness. Once you grasp these concepts you will teach them to others. You must learn to love unconditionally and without judgment. My role is to help you learn."

"That's a lot to absorb, Vida." I changed positions.

Vida took my hand in his and gently held it. "Yes, so we will continue to look at your life and your relationships to see how you have been up until now. You must change how you treat others in your life and you must change how you feel about yourself. Are you ready to continue?" He gave me a serious gaze and let go of my hand.

"But why me? What do I have to offer?" I am not sure I want the responsibility of teaching others.

"It is what you chose, Eric." Vida sounded sure.

"I chose?"

"Everyone chooses his or her path prior to coming to earth," he explained. "But let's save that for another visit. Let's get back to your relationships," Vida suggested.

"If you insist." I reluctantly agreed to continue, although I was skeptical about what he had just told me about teaching others.

Vida reviewed what I had said. "You were in Spokane. You achieved your goal of earning a six-figure income, yet you were not happy. You were in a marriage that had no intimacy and you met another woman who created feelings that you previously only felt in your dreams. As I recall, you felt connected to Donna like you felt connected in your dreams. Is that right?"

"Yes. That pretty well sums it up." I went back in my mind to that time. I felt frustrated that I was unable to figure out why I was so unhappy. "Why did I feel connected to Donna and not to Michele?" I asked.

"We should talk about being connected," Vida said as he sat in the chair again. "In the womb you were connected physically to your mother. Ages ago you were connected spiritually to your Creator. Separation occurred in both instances. The physical connection to your mother ended upon your physical birth and your spiritual connection to your Creator ended upon your spiritual birth, as told in the creation story in the book of Genesis in the Bible. You may recall from your religious studies that Adam and Eve were cast out of the Garden of Eden, where they enjoyed being in God's presence. Their banishment from the Garden represents mankind's fall in consciousness. The purpose of human life is to learn how to love so you can return to the Presence of the Creator.

"Since many men do not comprehend this, they seek connection elsewhere. They try to fit in with the pack, 'the guys'. They find a career where they can be 'successful,' that gives them a sense of being connected. Some men might try joining clubs, fraternal and religious organizations. They may also try alcohol or drugs to help them attain a feeling of being connected."

I had tried all those at one time or another. While I initially reached that feeling, it soon vanished and I had to try to get it again.

Vida walked across the room as he continued, "During adolescence, the male may attempt to connect through falling in love. He feels wonderful and complete and does things for his true love that demonstrates his affection. The feeling of falling in love is an ecstatic feeling. It is a feeling of being connected and complete. The feeling of completeness is something we do not want to let go of. The more incomplete we feel as an individual, the more we want to cling to our 'true love.' That is why some men become territorial and possessive with women. They do not want to lose the feeling of connection and completeness. They think they have a possession in their mate, a trophy for others to admire, a symbol of achievement they wear like battle ribbons on a soldier's uniform. The more power these men give their mates to make them feel complete, the better they initially feel. But like their other attempts at being connected, including alcohol and drugs, such a feeling is temporary."

How true, I thought. I could relate to the territorial bit and the trophy part. That's how I felt about my relationship with Sonnie.

Vida continued. "When a relationship evolves into marriage, some men begin to relax in their romantic behavior. They feel as though they have won the chase and have bagged their trophy. These men then turn their energy into other pursuits in life, because they know the trophy will always be there.

"The courtship stops and there is no intimacy. And from generation to generation this ritual of hunt, find and capture continues. Their role model of an adult relationship was what these men saw in their home, between their mother and father. Tell me about your parents Eric. How would you describe their marriage?" Vida held out his hands. "What were the male and female roles they played?"

"Well, let's see, they were married and...I don't remember much. They didn't go out on dates. Dad was a salesman and traveled weekly, and Mom stayed home to raise us kids. I thought it was pretty much … normal."

"Normal to you, perhaps, but was there intimacy?" he asked.

"I don't recall them holding hands and hugging and showing affection, if that's what you mean. I don't recall them sitting down to discuss matters." It now bothered me to realize that there was no intimacy in their marriage.

"So it's not surprising to you they eventually divorced?"

Vida knew. Sure he knew. Okay, so they got divorced. Was I surprised? As a teenager, I wondered at night about whether or not they would get divorced. Jimmy, one of my best friends, had parents who were divorced and he hated it. I wondered how it would be if my parents got divorced. Would I hate it? Would anyone feel sorry for me?

"No it's not surprising, but ... " I wanted to say more, but I stopped. In typical male fashion, I began to feel an emotion that scared me, in this case it was the pain of sadness, so I shut down.

"You don't have to say any more now," Vida said. "I am aware that it caused you a lot of pain. The point I want to make is; the marriage failed. When a relationship ends, the male often goes into a tailspin. When he feels himself sinking deep into despair and feels as though doom is apparent, he shuts down for self-preservation. He closes the door to his feelings and changes the lock. Rather than grieve his loss, he goes back to doing 'things' to keep his mind occupied, whether it's his work, his fraternal club, alcohol or drugs. He tries to fill what feels like a Hole in his Soul. These 'things' are temporary, quick fixes and although he may initially feel better, he will eventually feel worse."

"But why?" I asked. What Vida told me sounded and felt correct, but I needed to know the reason.

Vida sat in the chair again and said, "No Self. When there isn't anything that feels connected on the inside, then nothing on the outside can work. No matter how hard we try, it's not possible to connect when there is no Self. One does not feel complete by connecting to things on the outside. Because men generally deal with goals that are external, they tend to focus on external tasks that help them achieve their goals. By being busy and absorbed by these tasks, the male avoids the internal, and the internal is all the while crying, 'Take care of me! Find ME! FEED ME!'

Vida continued, "The Hole in the Soul is a hollow place where cold winds blow through and no matter how much one tries to fill it by being busy with external activities or by ingesting chemicals, it is still empty, barren and starved.

"One can't fix the feeling of fear and loneliness from having no Self, so many men turn to things they can control, or at least things that give them the illusion of control. The illusion makes these men think they can control their mate by attempting to control what she does, thinks and feels. Like someone who trains a dog to perform tricks, these men want everyone to see how well they control their mate." Vida paused and looked at me. He asked, "Can you control another's thoughts, feeling and emotions?"

"Are you saying I can't?" I always felt that as a salesman I could influence someone's behavior. Why not their thoughts as well?

"Have you been able to up until now, Eric?"

I thought a bit on that one. Did I try to control Michele? I was not clear on it. "I can't say for certain. Perhaps."

Vida leaned forward and asked, "Have you ever said to her, 'You shouldn't feel that way' or, 'How can you even think like that, after all I've done for you?' or, 'You owe it to me to ...' See what I mean? These are control issues." Vida had clarified it for me. Now I could see how I had attempted to control both Michele and Sonnie. I nodded in agreement. I had done that.

Vida spoke again. "The problem, is more complex than that. Once the relationship is over, some males tend not to complete the termination of it by going through a grieving process. You see, grief has several steps, and most men do not know how to work through them. They get hurt and angry when the relationship ends, and they simply cut it off without regard to their feelings. Grief work requires more than that. It is a process that works through the pain at the end of a relationship in order to mend the heart and to heal the mind.

"Grieving does not mean one dwells forever in one's pain. It involves feeling the pain and letting the anger out. Then one needs to move on. Acknowledging the good in the relationship, learning the lessons to be learned, forgiving the other person and letting go are necessary steps in the grieving process." Vida crossed his legs and kept speaking.

"Often, this does not happen. The feelings of hurt, anger and abandonment get buried so deep, one may be completely unaware of their existence. It is like buried garbage that one expects not to stink. Eventually, if enough garbage is buried in one place, not only will it stink, but also it will explode from the gases it builds. Buried feelings can manifest themselves through depression, irritability, anxiety, headaches and backaches.

"So the wounded male moves on, weary and weak, to the next activity. He carries his buried emotions with him. Since he does not have a healthy way to express himself, he simply moves on to whatever the next accomplishment is and loses himself in that. He is closed emotionally. When he enters into another relationship it is built on top of the previously incomplete, non-grieved relationships. He repeats the same pattern, yet he expects a different result. The buried emotions continue to rot inside him until the opportunity for release presents itself. The new relationship will suffer before it has an opportunity to flourish."

"So what can I do to prevent this from happening to me?" I certainly did not want to have any buried garbage destroy my relationship with Sonnie.

Vida stood and walked behind the chair, grabbed it, leaned forward and spoke in a whisper, "Find your Path."

"My path?"

"Your Path of Truth. Everyone has his, or her, own Path of Truth. One can follow many different paths, but one must eventually choose his, or her, Path of Truth."

"The Path of Truth?" I was skeptical, but Vida said nothing. "But how can you choose what you don't know?"

He walked around the chair, sat, leaned forward, legs apart and looked me in the eyes. "You did." He said with authority.

"What, chose the Path of Truth?"

"Your Path, not 'The Path.' There is no 'The Path,' there is only Your path."

"Vida, how could I have chosen my Path if I didn't know what my Truth was?"

"Our choices will bring us closer to our Truth if they come from in here." He placed his hand over his heart.

"All I want is happiness. Why am I miserable and confused?" I held my hands out in exasperation.

"You are at a turning point in your life, Eric. That's why I'm here, to guide you." As he spoke he stood by my side, placing his hand on my shoulder for comfort.

"So I chose to marry Michele." I said dejectedly.

He nodded in agreement.

"And Donna. I chose to meet her?"

"You could have met anyone, Eric. You were starving for intimacy with a woman. The Hole in your Soul has been crying for attention for years. You turned to religion to fill the Hole and when that failed, you turned to another woman. Now, how you feel confuses you. You are like a ship adrift at sea, caught in a storm, tossed to and fro. You are so out of touch with your inner Self, you will go wherever you think you feel a connection. Hence, you will remain confused. You lack inner clarity."

"So how do I get clear?" I sincerely wanted clarity.

"Go within." Vida touched my heart as he spoke.

"How?" That seemed unfeasible to me.

"Your Path is just that, a path, a way to your Truth."

"Where does it lead?" I wasn't sure I wanted to follow it.

"To your Truth. To the fulfillment of your creation."

"What do I do?" I asked in a somber tone.

"Move forward. Always ask for clarity, for Light, for direction. Resist making choices until you are clear."

"How will I know what choice is right?"

Vida took my hand again and placed it in his. "If it is for your Highest Good, you will experience feelings of peace and calm in your body. If it is not for your Good, then it is not your Truth, and you will have confused and chaotic thoughts. Truth always comes as a quiet, peaceful feeling. It is a still, small voice in your heart that speaks lovingly to you." He stopped speaking and released my hand.

"I need to be clear and to keep moving forward. Anything else?" I thought I'd better ask him now. I was nervous about taking the step, but I determined that it was better than remaining in my confused state of mind.

"Remember your dreams. Be more aware of them and try to write them down them." He sat at the foot of the bed.

"Dreams?" Now what was he saying? "Do I keep a journal?" I wanted to be sure I understood him precisely.

"Dreams always reveal your Truth. It is not possible for a dream to reveal anything that is not your personal Truth. By recording them, you can look back and contemplate their messages." He put one leg up on the bed. "Do you remember your dreams about the little boy?"

CONFESSIONS OF A CLOSED MALE

"The one where he was singing?"

"Yes, and the others too. Like the one where he was hiding in a kitchen cabinet and drowning."

"Sure I remember. I was terrified of them. But how do they show me my Truth?"

"The little boy is you, Eric, the essence of you. The child is hidden in a kitchen cabinet. The kitchen, a place of preparing food for the body's nourishment, represents a place in you where the Universe prepares nourishment for your Soul. The cabinet represents the organized way you compartmentalize various parts of your life. The little boy Eric has been waiting for the adult Eric to find him, and when you did, you felt helpless. You stood by watching the little boy Eric get closer and closer to death. Finally you stopped the boy's death by waking up physically. In truth, you need to wake up spiritually."

"So, Eric," Vida looked directly at me, and our eyes connected.

"Yeah," I answered solemnly.

Vida jumped up, "Wake up! I am here, and it's safe. Move forward."

I didn't know what to do, so I laid in my bed and thought about my dreams. I felt the sadness of the little boy and as I did, a sense of sadness grew in me until I felt overwhelmed. I sat up and leaned toward Vida. Maintaining direct eye contact with me, he took a couple of steps toward the head of my bed. I held out my arms and we hugged. Tears formed in my eyes. My body quivered with emotion. The embrace comforted me as I felt Vida's unconditional love envelop me.

Then quietly Vida whispered in my ear, "It's okay, it's safe, go ahead and feel whatever it is that is coming up."

And I felt it. I cried as I felt myself let go of stuff that I had been holding in all my life, heavy, dark, ugly, energy.

I cried heavily from the dark recesses of my soul. The energy that flowed out of my gut was like a swift roaring river, as feelings deep inside me finally gushed out. I have no idea how long it lasted. Time may have been suspended, or it may have been two days, the point is, it didn't matter. It was okay. I felt safe enough to cry.

When I finally stopped, we sat on the bed in silence for several minutes. Eventually Vida gently said "Eric, if it's okay with you, it's time for me to go." We let go of one another and I wiped my eyes with my sheets, grabbed a tissue and blew my nose.

"Why now?" I had just experienced a release of pent-up feelings and I was reluctant to have him leave.

"Because it's time. I will return."

"When?" I asked with distress in my voice.

"I will come back tomorrow, Eric. You are in a safe place. Rest and think about what I have said to you. You have lessons to learn as you move forward on your Path. Remember that my job is to guide you. You will learn through your experiences."

With that, Vida let go, turned to the door and disappeared.

A nurse came into the room to check my vital signs and to change the IV bottle. "Have you been crying, Mr. Crane?"

"Yes, but I am okay." In my male-ness I minimized the situation. I was not used to crying as an adult, much less in front of someone I did not know.

"Everything is okay, Mr. Crane. You'll be out of here in no time." She attempted to reassure me.

"Thanks." I tried to sound appreciative of her efforts.

"Can I get you anything?" She asked compassionately.

"Yes. I would like something to write on if you don't mind." I began to regain my composure.

"Not at all, I'll be back in a few minutes after I finish with my other patients." And with that she left my room.

I did not want to be alone, so I called out, "Abliel?" I summoned him with a trembling voice.

"Yes, Eric." He replied in his usual loving manner.

"Who is Vida, and where does he come from?"

"He is one of us, a Spirit Guide sent to teach you. He comes from a sphere of consciousness a little higher than the earth plane."

"Ah!" I did not know about other spheres of existence.

"You will learn much, Eric. The lessons will come to you in dreams and your life experiences. Your Guides will assist you in understanding the lessons. Be receptive and have an open heart. This process will continue through all of your life. For now, just rest here and listen to your Spirit Teachers and Guides. Rest and listen. That is all."

I could see out my window that it was dark and the fatigue in my body told me it was late. I decided to go to sleep. As I rolled over, the telephone rang. It was Sonnie.

– *Four* –

"I COULDN'T GET A BABY-SITTER, SO I THOUGHT I'D BETTER CALL."
Sonnie seldom said "hello" when she spoke on the phone. She simply
started her sentence as if the conversation had been in progress for
sometime.

"Hi, Wook." I chose not to tell her I was sleepy because I wanted to
talk to her.

"So, how was the rest of your day? Have you been visited again by
your angel?" Her tone was playful.

"Actually, I was just speaking to him." I wanted to sound convincing
because I was not sure she believed me.

"Oh, hope I didn't interrupt?" she said politely.

"No, no. He left before you called." I thought for a moment about
what I wanted to tell her. She had not heard about Vida yet. Maybe I
should start there.

"I want to talk to you about something." I figured I might as well
tell her. "Abliel told me I was going to be visited by a Teacher, and I
have." I got quiet on the last phrase. My confidence in speaking about
my new experience was low, due to its newness.

"A teacher?" There was a hint of amusement in her voice.

"He's a Spirit Guide. His name is Vida, and he came here soon after
you left this morning."

"Oh, a Spirit Guide, how interesting." I could tell by the patroniz-
ing tone of her voice that she did not believe me.

"This may sound kind of crazy to you, but please give me a few minutes to tell you what he had to say."

"Okay." She sighed. Perhaps she did not want to spend much time on the phone. But nonetheless, I felt it important to tell her about what I had learned from Vida.

I recounted to Sonnie the conversation Vida and I had regarding my image of a wife and how there was no intimacy in my relationship with Michele.

"That's an interesting discovery Eric." She sounded more sincere now. I had her attention.

"I learned that what another person thinks and feels about a situation is just as important as what I think."

"What do you mean?"

"You know, like when I took the job at Systech, I mentally accepted the offer and decided to move before I really talked it over with Michele. When we did talk about it, I didn't give her an opportunity to fully share her feelings about moving. Is this making any sense to you?"

"Why yes. I'm glad you see that because you treat me like that too. What else did you learn?" Sonnie is curious.

"I discovered that I don't see the other person in the relationship for who they really are. I have my own image of what they should be and I expect them to fit my image."

"And what's that?"

"The image I wanted Michele to fill was my dysfunctional image of a wife, a domestic worker and a caretaker for my children." I waited to see if she now comprehended.

"That, too is how I feel about being your wife, Eric. I feel like I can't measure up to what you want me to be.

"I am going to change that, Wook. Vida is helping me understand so many wonderful concepts about relationships and who I truly am. He is helping me learn to love unconditionally."

There was silence on the phone. I waited anxiously for Sonnie's response.

"Hummm. That sounds profound," she said quietly. "Tell me his name again." She got louder

"Vida."

"Well, tell Vida I appreciate him. Are there any more visits planned?"

"He said he would return tomorrow." I was relieved to hear belief in her voice.

"I can't wait to hear what you discuss next." Sonnie's words were heartfelt.

"Me either. How was your day?" I felt it best to change the subject to something lighter. All of this was new to me and I was beginning to feel apprehensive about going into more detail without seeing her reactions.

She proceeded to tell me about what she and the kids had been doing and the list of household chores she had done and the phone calls she had made. In true Sonnie fashion, most days were run on the red line. No taking it slow for her. She talked like she lived, fast.

"Sounds like you've had quite a day. I bet you're tired from all you've done." I wanted her to know that I truly cared.

"Why thanks, Eric. Yes, I am tired, and I guess from all that you've been through that you are, too."

"Yep. I'm ready for sleep." I yawned as I said that.

"Okay. Well, I guess I'll see you tomorrow. I'll call before I come, okay?" Her voice perked up.

"Sounds great. I love you, Sonnie."

"I love you too, Eric," she said affectionately.

I hung up the phone, rolled over and turned off the lights. I thought about the phone call. I felt Sonnie originally thought I was making this up. But why? She believed in angels, she also had psychic readings done for her in the past. Why did she sound skeptical? Maybe what I said surprised her. Our marriage had drifted due to my lack of communication. Perhaps hearing my extraordinary account of the past couple of days, gave her hope that I might change. She was also prone to second guessing my motives. Whatever, I told her the truth, and that was the end of it. I turned over and drifted off into a deep sleep.

The next morning, I woke up to see Vida sitting in my chair.

"Good morning, Eric. Sleep well?"

"Vida." I was surprised to see him. I could not read the clock on the wall, as I did not have my glasses on. "Do you know what time it is?"

"Six-thirty," Vida replied with no expression in his voice.

"Man." I rubbed my eyes and stretched. "I'm going to ring for coffee." I called the nurse's station.

"Yes?" An anonymous voice responded.

"May I have a cup of coffee?" I said in my deep baritone morning voice.

"Breakfast is coming at seven, can you wait until then?"

"Yeah, sure." I looked at Vida as if to say "oh, well."

"You could have said you wanted some now," he said nonchalantly.

"Yeah, I know, but I don't mind. I'm going to get cleaned up." I had been told that I could get up and move around, all I had to do was take the IV stand with me. I got up, covered up my backside, because the hospital gown left me exposed, and walked into the bathroom. When I came out, Vida was standing by the window.

"So Vida, what's on our agenda today?" I asked humorously.

He turned and walked back to the chair. "Let's pick up where we left off yesterday."

"You mean the dream?" My tone was somber. Yesterday's discussion of the dream brought up deep seated emotion. I wasn't sure I wanted to go there again. I crawled back into my bed and pulled up the sheets.

"You cried. Do you know what that was all about?"

I thought for a moment. "What you said about the boy felt so true. It must have triggered feelings within me."

"It felt sad, Eric." Vida was quiet.

"Yeah, it does." I got quiet too. I was not ready to feel those feelings again. Vida must have sensed how I felt.

"Let's go back to Spokane." He quickly said. "What did you do when you left Donna's house after the first visit?"

"Please understand Vida, I had met 'another woman' for the first time since my marriage to Michele. My feelings were out of control. I wanted to be with Donna, in fact, I was obsessed about seeing her. I returned to her house the next day, and talked about what we should do. Neither of us wanted anyone to get hurt by pursuing a relationship. Yet we both felt a strong attraction to one another. While we were on her couch, we hugged one another, and then we kissed."

"You kissed?" Vida's expression indicated he suspected there was more that I was not telling him.

"Yeah, a kiss. We talked and then we started kissing on her sofa. It went on for some time. It was heavy French kissing. Our passion ran rampant. My heart pounded as blood ran hot throughout my body. For several days we repeated the scene. Talking, and making out."

"And sex?" Vida's tone was politely discrete.

"We didn't have sex, initially, beyond necking and petting. We gave each other massages, hugged and kissed, but no sexual intercourse. Not that we didn't want to, we did, but I couldn't go that far, not yet. Mormons believe adultery is an extremely serious transgression."

"So what did you do?" Vida asked without judgement.

"For the next few weeks, I felt lost and confused about my relationship with Donna and Michele. I was ridden with thoughts of being with Donna, yet I felt guilty about not wanting to be with Michele. In my confused state of emotions I was desperately looking for a sign that could give me an insight to what was going on. Up until then, I had been living what seemed to me to be a normal everyday sort of life, and in a flash, my world turned upside down. I was crazy about Donna and that was not supposed to happen to this married Mormon man, yet it did happen and I was confused about my feelings for Michele and Donna. "Was I 'in love', or was it simply some silly sort of temporary feeling that would soon pass?

"I wanted answers, and I wanted them fast. I felt I might lose my marriage and the most beautiful children in the world." I changed my position in the bed as I spoke. Vida made no effort to speak, so I continued with my account.

"I went to see my Bishop in hope of finding an answer to my problem. I told him about Donna. He was disturbed about what he heard, and felt I was in spiritual danger for breaking the church's commandments regarding marital fidelity. He referred me to a Mormon psychiatrist who specialized in marital and family therapy and warned me to stop seeing Donna.

"Dr. Bronson is the name of the psychiatrist. He was a conservative man in his mid to late fifties with a soft, pudgy, round belly. His hairstyle was popular for the fifties, cut by a barber, not a stylist, slicked down with hair creme. He had silver hair; rectangular, silver-colored wire-rimmed glasses; and wore a poly blend short-sleeve shirt with an ugly blue-and-silver-striped clip-on tie like you might get at a discount department store with blue-light specials. To top it off, he wore cowboy boots, the cheap kind that had a gloss to them, without the first briar cut or sagebrush burn. No self-respecting man would ever wear cowboy boots didn't have range scars."

Vida yawned and put his hand up to cover his mouth but said nothing. I paused for a moment and thought back to that day in his office. I continued to tell Vida my story.

"His office was dark and shadowy, with piles of files on his steel gray desk and volumes of books, some standing up and some stacked flat. There was a feeling of cold darkness, not in temperature but in spirit. An uneasy feeling filled my gut but I attributed it to being nervous about seeing a psychiatrist for the first time in my life. Anyway, I was confused and had agreed with the Bishop that professional help was necessary. So I reassured myself that it would be okay to stay.

I recalled Dr. Bronson's words: "So Mr. Crane, tell me why you are here." He said in a condescending tone as he peered over his glasses.

I told him my story. "I'm a father of three precious children and have been married for thirteen years. I've been a faithful and active member of the church. I've worked hard at my job and have done well. I've never in any way been unfaithful to my marriage vows.

"Several weeks ago, I met another woman. I find myself extremely attracted to her, and think that I might even be in love with her.

"I'm confused about all of this, and I can't get clear on what to do, so I guess that's why I am here - to get clear."

"Well Mr. Crane, this is a serious matter. Unfortunately it happens to many men, in fact, over the years I've had several women to whom I felt attracted. One woman in particular was quite attractive to me, and if I saw her today, I would have strong feelings. But I've had to control my feelings and do what is right for my wife and my family, so I repented and flew straight.

"Now that's what you have to do, Mr. Crane. You need to remember who you are and that you are married and a father. What would happen to them if you left them for another woman?

"You need to repent. You need to remember who God is and who you are. God gave you a wife. Like the scripture says; *Cleave unto her and no one else*. If you do this now, if you cut off this affair, the feelings for that other woman will go away, and things will return to normal."

I turned to Vida. "My blood was boiling. I was furious at what I just heard from that arrogant man. Can you imagine?"

Vida shook his head in apparent disbelief. I then resumed.

"The session was over and he asked me for his fee."

"Could you please bill me?" I tried to sound polite, although inside I was seething.

"I suppose so, but next time, please be prepared to pay at the end of the visit. Now, when would you like your next appointment? How about next Thursday?" He looked at his appointment book and began to schedule the next visit. His tone was presumptuous.

"I have a busy travel schedule for the next few weeks. How about I go back to my office, check out my schedule and call you back?" I had no intention of ever calling him back.

"That will be fine, Mr. Crane. Here's my card." His arrogance was nauseating.

"I stood up and bolted for the door. No hand shake, no more words. My sole objective was to get the hell out of there as fast as I could."

I looked over at Vida. He had a cat-that-ate-the-canary grin on his face.

"Then what?" He was obviously amused at all of this. At least Spirit Guides have a sense of humor, I thought. I of course was not feeling like this was one bit funny.

"I got into my car to go home. I was royally pissed off. What right did that pompous south-end-of-a-mule have to tell me that I needed to repent and do what was right for everyone else? What about me and how I felt? I didn't want everything to return to normal. 'NORMAL' *obviously* was not working!

"There I was, in my car, furious, driving like a mad-man. I screamed as loud as I could, 'UP YOURS DR. BRONSON! WHO THE HELL MADE YOU GOD !!!' I cursed Dr. Bronson, God and the Church. How could a professional tell a patient something like that?"

I looked to Vida for validation. His stoic face told me to continue.

"Was the doctor there to judge or to heal? What about all those 'blessings' the church promised if I faithfully obeyed their 'Commandments'. I was a dues-paying, card-carrying member of the Church and defended it in public and private. And God? Where was God? At the most chaotic and confused time of my life where was this God I had worshiped for the past fifteen years?"

"You were mad at Dr. Bronson, *and* the Church?" Vida asked.

"That's right. I swore I would never return to Dr. Bronson nor would I ever go to the Church again, because if all they could do was treat me like a condemned person, they could all go to hell. If heaven was made up of people like that, I would just as soon go to hell myself."

"Guess you showed them." Vida's tone was cynical. I was getting used to his sense of humor. I decided to ignore him and to keep going with my story. Telling it to him made me feel better.

"Anyway, a few days later, I cooled off. It was apparent to me that I needed help, because I was more confused than ever. I was falling in love with a woman who was not my wife, and though I felt it was wrong morally and socially, it was nonetheless very real. I wanted to stop the world and think for a few days, but that didn't happen."

"Why not?" Vida asked with a smile.

"Because I can't stop the world, Vida," I said with sarcasm. I smiled a cute sarcastic smile at him and continued. He shrugged his shoulders as I spoke.

"I couldn't think, I couldn't sleep, I couldn't work. I tried to pray for answers, but that didn't work either. I wanted to keep my family intact and have Donna too. The feeling of being in love was so great that I could not focus on anything but being with her. I was dazed and confused. Events felt like they were happening at warp speed. For the first time in my adult life, my mind felt out of control, and I feared and loathed that feeling. I needed help but I couldn't get it from the church or from the church's rec-ommendation. I couldn't talk to Michele or my boss. I was in a new town and had only one friend, Stu Wilson, whom I met at church. Stu and I were close in age. He had a thriving medical practice and four children. I admired him as a successful man, so I decided to give him a call."

"You thought Stu could help?" Vida asked with a sincere tone. "Even though he is a Mormon who might have an opinion similar to your bishop?"

"Yeah, I did." Being fairly new to Spokane, my acquaintances were limited to the church and the office. So I called Stu. We agreed to meet for lunch the following Wednesday at The Grille, a trendy lunch spot in Spokane. We started out with the usual small talk about the weather, kids and football, then I led into what we were really there for. I explained my feelings toward Donna to him and my confusion about what to do about the situation. Then I told him about my visit with Dr. Bronson. Stu was shocked to hear my story, but he listened patiently the way a good doctor does.

Our conversation blended into the lunch time noise of the busy restaurant: "So, I don't know Stu, I thought that maybe you might understand. You must see a lot of women in your practice. Have you ever been attracted to one of them?"

"Yep. It's happened, but I didn't fall in love with her. At least that's what I tell myself." He sounded unsure.

"Yeah, I know. I mean I don't fall in love with every good-looking woman I meet. Why, I wasn't even looking for another woman, this happened so quickly," I rationalized.

"Eric, there is a difference between being in love and loving someone. Love is something that takes commitment, effort and responsibility. Being in love, well, its not like puppy love. There's a book you should probably read that explains this sort of stuff better than I can. It's called *A Road Less Traveled*. You really should look into it."

"Thanks, I will." I wrote the name of the book on my business card. What Stu said about commitment and responsibility did not ring true to me. "I've been responsible and committed for thirteen years, and I never felt the passion I now feel for Donna, with Michele. I don't think I ever felt like I fell in love with Michele. It felt more like a duty to me. But with Donna, when I sit in my easy chair at home, I fantasize about her entering the room. I can't wait to see her again and to smell her hair and touch her." Stu's face changed to a puzzled look. Perhaps he did not understand after all.

We continued our conversation. Stu listened attentively as I told him my story. Finally, with the food eaten, we looked at one another in a moment of awkward silence.

I spoke next. "So, want some dessert?"

"No thanks, I've got to get back to the office. I have a lot of appointments this afternoon and church meetings tonight. But how about golf sometime?" Stu reached over and took the check and left twenty dollars on the table. "My treat today."

"Thanks. And golf sounds great!" I said as I stood.

"I'll call the club, get a tee time and let you know." Stu said as he walked toward the front door.

"Looking forward to it. Thanks for lunch, Stu."

"No problem. It's good to see you. Tell Michele 'hello' for me." We shook hands and went our separate ways. I took the long way back to the office, thinking about what Stu said.

I paused for a moment, and looked at Vida. "I'd tried for thirteen years to love Michele and, in fact, I did love certain aspects of her. She was an excellent mother, and she spent a great deal of time with our children. She was a devoted wife who followed me in my career without question. Yet I would never have called my feeling for her 'being in love.' With her I never had the excitement and thrill I had experienced with Donna. I didn't like being close and intimate with Michele. Perhaps I didn't know how. Maybe I wouldn't allow it. But for whatever reason, I was not intimate with Michele."

"It probably has to do with the image you wanted her to fill. Who would want to be intimate with that image?" Vida's tone implied a negative response.

"Good point. But, now I'd met a woman who changed that. For the first time, I felt comfortable being close. I felt connected and complete and energized by simply being in her presence, as opposed to the drained and empty feeling I got with Michele, so I was hopelessly confused."

"She held the image of passion, and you felt like you had to make a choice." Vida held out one hand. "Michele over here, and Donna," he held out his other hand, "over there."

"Right. Why couldn't I feel the way I felt about Donna with Michele? Did I want to? Was it possible? Is there such a thing as chemistry that makes it easier for some people to be intimate than it does for others? I felt connected with Donna and disconnected with Michele. Why? Was it worth leaving one for the other?"

"You mean, one image for another?" Vida asked.

"That sounds so trite." I looked away.

"You obviously came to a decision. How'd you do that?"

"I saw a therapist."

My thoughts went back to Spokane. Donna had been in therapy for over a year and she suggested I consider it for myself. She gave me a business card of someone she highly regarded. At that time, I had no respect for Dr. Bronson, so I was open to her recommendation.

That Monday morning, I went to the office and avoided the usual political rounds. I took out the business card Donna had given to me.

> **AMY CARLSON, MSW, LCSW**
>
> *Family Certified Therapist*
>
> ⤳
>
> 1225 Riverside Dr., Suite 244
> Spokane, WA 94808
> (503) 555-7522

I picked up the telephone and dialed the number. It rang four times. "Not meant to be," I thought. Relieved, I was ready to hang up when I heard a female voice say, "Good morning. Ms. Carlson's office."

"Uh, yes, uh, I'd like to speak to Ms. Carlson please."

"She's with a client. Would you like to schedule an appointment?"

"Uh, sure, I mean, I suppose so." I tapped the desk with my pen.

"What's a good time for you?"

"Whenever you have another opening."

"How about after lunch today?"

"I agreed and gave her my name and phone number and hung up." I paused, then I turned to Vida, "I followed my gut! I paid attention to how I felt, and acted accordingly."

"Amazing," was Vida's emotionless response.

"Yeah, I suppose so." I agreed in a proud tone.

"Tell you what, Eric. Continue thinking about what happened next. I'm going to leave. When I return we will discuss it." He stood as he spoke. By now I was used to Vida leaving in what seemed like the middle of our conversation, but I was learning to trust his judgement.

"Fair enough." I said.

Vida departed and I continued to reminisce. My thoughts took me back to the day of my session with Amy.

As I entered her office, I immediately felt at ease and took that as a good sign. The office was light and it looked and felt like walking into someone's home. The atmosphere was professional, yet very personable, and warm in spirit. Amy greeted me with a warm handshake.

"Hello, my name is Amy Carlson, I'm glad you're here!"

"Eric. Eric Crane."

"Come on in." She motioned toward her office. I felt as though I were in her home. She had an oak roll-top desk with a cane-back chair. A blue floral couch with three throw pillows lined the left wall, where I sat. Amy sat in a rocking chair. JFK used to sit in a rocking chair. "So what?" I thought. I often had stray thoughts enter my mind that had nothing to do with what was going on at the time. I noticed only a few books on her bookcase and a few pictures on the wall. Prints mostly, watercolors, one original. A rose garden at that.

"So, Eric, what's going on in your life?"

I thought *Ha! Are you kidding!* But I said, "I don't know where to start."

"Just go with the first thing that comes to mind." She had a soft tone that felt compassionate. Her face showed no tension, only empathy.

I began to talk. I told her the same thing I told Dr. Bronson. The difference was I felt more at ease in Amy's office. For starters, she called me Eric rather than Mr. Crane.

After I finished, she looked at me. "Tell me about your marriage, Eric," she said.

"We met one summer while we were both working at Jackson Lake Lodge in the Grand Teton National Park. I was doing a summer student ministry program that involved two Sunday worship services and a devotional on Wednesday. The interdenominational Christian ministry was for tourists as well as employees.

"Michele and I met each other while working there and we began dating. Eventually we had sex. Although I had made a pact with God that I would not have sex again until I was married, our heated feelings were too great, and I gave in. Later, I felt guilty about it and felt like I ought to marry her to keep my agreement with God.

"As it turned out, Michele got pregnant and we felt so guilty that we decided to get married. I converted to her religion and we moved to Virginia. Our Bishop married us, because, as he said, 'Better to be married than to live in sin.' I was twenty-one and she was twenty-three. A month later, Michele miscarried.

"The church had a lay ministry only, and there is no job market for someone with a religion degree, so I went to work as a home improvement salesman. After the first year of marriage, we had our first child, Felicia.

"A year later, I changed jobs to selling life insurance, because I felt

CONFESSIONS OF A CLOSED MALE

like at least I was helping people by preparing their family financially for death. Besides, we needed more money, and I was convinced that selling life insurance would pay more. After a year, our second child was born, Michael.

"Michele had been missing her family for some time, so when Michael was a little more than a year old, we decided to move west, and I found a job in Denver selling insurance.

"Erica was born about a year later, and at that time, I decided to get into the computer business. It seemed like the place to be. I asked a guy at our church who was in the computer business if he could give me some advice about it, and he suggested that I go to work for him, because he needed a sales rep. After about seven years of that, I ended up here."

"But what about your marriage?"

"What about it?" I was lost.

"I asked you to tell me about your marriage."

"Oh, well I thought I did."

"Do you like being married?" She emphasized the word "like."

"I suppose it's all-right. It's something you have to do, eventually."

"Is it fun?" Amy held out her hand.

"Fun? Hell, no. Marriage isn't fun, its hard work!"

"Tell me about Donna."

"Donna, yes well, Donna is different. She's fun, she's, well, I suppose I have real strong feelings for her, and I may even be in love with her."

"Eric, when you spoke about Michele, your face appeared tight and tense, with a sort of frown to it, but when you spoke of Donna, your face changed. It was at ease, light, free of tension and it was obvious that you do have some very strong feelings. I can see you are confused. Let's work on getting you clear on how you really feel, okay?"

That felt good, and I agreed. We set another appointment for two days out. I left thinking that at last I was moving in the right direction.

The next few days were fairly routine. Nothing much changed except that I was getting more and more confused. Like the fog blowing in on San Francisco, confusion swept over the many emotions I felt, which prevented clarity in my mind.

During our next session Amy asked me how I felt. A simple enough question but I had difficulty answering it.

"What do you mean?" I asked with bewilderment.

"How do you feel right now?" She asked, leaning slightly forward.

"Okay I guess..." I wasn't sure what she meant. I felt okay. I ate lunch, work was okay, there was no big thing going on at home (other than the fact that I was considering having an affair!) so I felt okay.

Amy gave me a look like "Ah, come on, cut the crap, answer the question," and I looked at her with what must have been one of the blankest expressions she had ever seen. I truly had no idea what she meant.

"Eric, you've got to feel something."

"Like what?" I had no clue.

"Angry, confused, happy, sad, pissed off, something!"

"Oh, that - well I feel confused, I guess" I wasn't sure how I felt. In fact, it had been so long since someone asked me how I felt and really expected an honest answer. I mean people asked me for my opinion and whenever I was sick, the children and Michele would ask me how I felt, but no one ever seemed interested in my feelings.

"Confused and what? Is that all?" Amy had a fervent expression on her face.

"Well," I said it again. "I suppose I feel something else, but I'm not sure what it is because I'm so confused!"

"Can you draw it?" She smiled.

"What?" What was she asking? Draw my feelings? "Are you serious?"

"When we ask children about their feelings, they generally cannot express them, so we ask them to draw their feelings in the form of a picture. Can you draw your feelings and make them into a picture?"

I smiled and laughed. I felt stupid. There I was, a grown man, and I could not express my feelings, so she wanted me to draw a picture, as if I were a child! Man alive! What nerve, suggesting that I, Eric Crane, should have to resort to tactics designed for children to express my feelings! But there I was, thirty-four years of age, and I had no idea how to express my feelings. It was a sad commentary on where I was in my life. Out of touch, out of control and totally confused.

"I don't know. I've never done this before. I mean, who gives a rat's ass about how I feel?" I slumped into the couch.

"Do you, Eric?" Amy asked.

Therapy can be tough. You get asked questions you'd rather not answer. That was one of them. I would have liked to avoid answering it, but I knew I could not. I looked down at the carpet as I formulated my response. Eye contact was impossible at that moment. "Yeah, I suppose I do," I said somberly.

"I tell you what Eric, just close your eyes and tell me what you see."

With mixed emotions of fear and reluctance, I closed my eyes. I got real quiet and still and let my thoughts go. I waited. She waited. Then, ever so slightly, a picture began forming in my mind. My words were slow and broken, "There are clouds, storm clouds, and they are building up into big, billowy, dark, sinister clouds." I paused, as I was not sure this was what she had in mind. Amy spoke next.

"What color are they? Describe every detail."

"They're dark, dark and gray and deep blue with purple and bits of white around the edges. They are low and forming fast, like a big thunderstorm about to blow in. The bottoms are billowy and rough. There are so many that the sky is dark. The sun has disappeared behind them, and the wind is blowing right through me." I felt my stomach tremble.

"What is the blue and the dark?" Amy was directing me through the process.

"Rain." My tone was quiet and subdued, kind of automatic.

"What is the white?"

"Lightning."

"What happens if they break?"

"It will rain, storm, a bad storm, a violent storm, like a tornado!"

"And the lightning?" Amy asked.

"It will crack with a loud, booming explosion that will rattle the earth and tingle with electricity."

"Why don't they break?"

"People will get hurt!" I now felt scared.

"Who?"

"My children!" I was horrified to think that harm may come to them.

"What will happen to them?" Her question made me think.

"They will get hurt! There is no one to protect them! The storm could wash them away!" Horror ran through me.

"Then how can they be safe?"

"I must shelter them. I must put them in a safe place out of the storm's way."

"If they were safe and it were to storm, what would happen?"

"They'd be okay. It would storm and then, it would be over."

"And after the storm?" she asked.

I paused to think for a few moments. What happens after a storm? "A storm cleanses. It washes away the old and dirty and brings new life. It's part of nature. Storms are good, but they can cause damage in the process."

"But, they are good?" She confirmed.

"Yes, they are good." I said quietly.

"So do it, Eric. Put the children in a safe place and let it storm," Amy encouraged.

So I did. I found a safe place under the leaf of a giant flower up on top of a hill. I instructed them to wait there. I felt they were safe. Then the clouds burst.

Amy must have known what was about to happen, because she handed me a box of tissues and a stuffed bear. I grabbed the bear and hugged it and cried violently and uncontrollably. I screamed from the innermost part of my soul, from a place I did not know existed. A forgotten place inside had opened up, and a lot of stuff was coming out. The sounds coming from my gut were the sounds of thunder. They cracked and were loud and powerful. The tears were like sheets of rain falling hard and driven by the force of anger and rage.

The storm continued, and for a while, I thought all was going to be destroyed and lost. The winds of anger increased to tornadic force. It sounded like a locomotive was coming through the room. I was gasping for air as I let out another guttural yell.

The tissues were disappearing quickly, one after another. The brown bear I was clutching was wet with tears and bent from being squeezed and wrenched.

Finally, it ended. The storm had passed. The sun followed in its trail. I regained my composure, looked at Amy and sank into the couch.

"Are you okay?" Amy asked with compassion.

I had no energy left for speech, so I whispered, "Yeah."

"Where are you now?" She leaned forward.

"Here."

Leaning further, she touched my hand. "Do you want to stop?"

"Yeah." I felt relieved.

My thoughts were interrupted as two hospital volunteers came into the room. One of them spoke, "Would you like a magazine or a book, Mr. Crane?"

"No thank you." I replied absently.

Vida entered the room, but the volunteers could not see him. They continued with their duties.

"Okay, just give us a call if you change your mind," the same volunteer said. And with that, they left the room.

I turned to Vida. "It never ceases to amaze me that I'm the only one who sees you. It's hard to get used to."

Vida smiled. He took a set in the chair, stretched out his legs, folded his arms across his chest and said, "You get used to it after a while."

"It seems all so far away in the past, yet somehow it's like it was yesterday. My life had seemed to be going quite well, up until we moved to Spokane. Meeting Donna and falling in love with her had changed everything."

"You awoke to your feelings." Vida placed his hand over his heart. "You chose to open up and feel."

"I chose to?" I thought about that. I suppose I did. "You're right, I did make a choice, didn't I?" Choosing was a concept I was unfamiliar with.

I thought how my visits to Amy's office changed me. For the first time in my adult life, I got in touch with my true feelings. So what if it was done at a child's level? At least I had done it, and I was on my way to becoming clear and eliminating some confusion. For the first time, I had chosen to open up. Even if it was for a brief moment, at least I made the choice to do it.

It was a choice! I could choose to open up and feel my feelings! Why it's so simple! But now what?

I was still confused. "I felt better, because I had opened up and let some feelings out that I didn't know existed. Could it be that simple?" I asked.

"We often disown our feelings, place them in a lost-and-found department at the bottom of our being. You had a lot of feelings stuffed down there, and perhaps you still do." Vida reached in his pocket, pulled something out and jiggled it around in his hand. I could not see what it was. "All feelings are for our good. They reveal to us matters of the Soul. It's a shame that most men choose to stuff them."

"Choose to stuff them? Now wait a minute. I didn't know the difference. Why I - "

Vida interrupted, "You can feel them if you want to. The problem with some men is they stuff their feelings deep in their guts and pretend they no longer exist. They ignore them and therefore they ignore their Soul. Therefore, the Hole gets bigger.

"Most men live life not knowing how to be in touch with their feelings. In fact, many of them don't even know they can feel anything other than sad, angry or tired.

"They tend to greet each other with something like: 'Hello Jim, how are you today?'

"Oh, just fine, Stan, and you?"

"Never better!" Vida paused.

"What would it be like if they said: 'Good morning Frank, I feel guilty this morning because I yelled at my son for not picking up his socks. What about you?'

"Well Bob, to tell you the truth, I feel truly serene today. The sunrise was spectacular, and I was in awe of the majesty of it all. In fact, I wrote a poem about it.'

"You see, Eric, men don't do that because they have been socialized as males by your society, and males in your society don't go around talking like that. But they could, if you all choose to change your society's rules."

"Are you kidding? Who would ever say things like that?"

"We used to." He said as if it were totally so.

"Huh? What do you mean 'used to'?"

"A long time ago, before recorded history, we lived in a civilization where we talked openly about our feelings and matters of the Soul."

"Where was that?"

"Another time, Eric. Today you must learn to be open to your feelings. Until that visit to Amy's, you were completely out of touch with them. The truth is, you did get in touch with your feelings. You became aware of a notion in your Soul."

"What do you mean?"

"Donna."

I paused for a moment, "Oh, you mean those feelings. Sure I felt *those* feelings."

"One way or another, we feel. But too often we don't want to own our feelings. The Soul continues to be forgotten. That's what has happened to you over the years, Eric. You have not allowed yourself to acknowledge your feelings. Your Soul has been like the little boy trapped under the sink, crying out for help. Right or wrong, the affair with Donna woke you up."

I sensed he was speaking truthfully. "Vida you're right, because I feel it in here." I moved my hand to the center of my ribs, just above my stomach. "I actually feel a warm sensation here that tells me you are correct! But why is it so hard to acknowledge my feelings? And why am I not open and in touch with them?"

"It's like a rose, Eric."

"A rose?" Now where is he going? I thought to myself.

He held out his hand, which held red rose petals.

"It's like a rose." Vida stood and placed the petals on the bed. "Of all the varieties of flowers, the rose is the most delicate and beautiful with a sweet bouquet. Its petals are exquisite with a texture of silk and velvet. It's alive with color.

"But, it is when the rose is open that it is best admired for its true beauty. While a rose as a bud is pretty, it's not until it opens that it changes and realizes its potential for which it is created.

"Only when a rose is in full bloom, can one see inside and see its essence and its most vibrant color. This is why the rose is uniquely beautiful among all other flowers, because when the rose is fully exposed, it has so much more to it, and its beauty fills the space in which it exists."

I shifted my position in the bed. "So, like the rose, we're the most beautiful when we're open?"

"Are all not from the same Creator?" Vida moved away.

"You aren't going to start getting religious, are you?"

"It has nothing to do with religion, Eric. It's nature. It is Truth. It is how it is, and that's all it is." He gave me what I call the serious look. Loving, but serious.

"I'm sorry, it's just that right now I don't want religion. I've had religion out the wazoo and I need a break."

"We are discussing a concept about being open and aware of our feelings. We can never fulfill who we are created to be until we remove our veneer, exposing the authentic Self for all to see. At the core lies our Soul."

"So why aren't we always open?" I asked.

"It's a mystery. We are created to enjoy life. That means we should have joy, should feel joy and be joyful. Like all nature, we can only find our joy in being who we have been created to be, our True Self. Like the rose, we are our best when we fulfill our creation through being open.

Vida continued to speak. "Our Soul is authentic. It knows nothing about covering up and closing down. That's the work of the Ego, the false self. Our Ego keeps the Soul at bay due to its fear of being replaced. It learns how to survive in a world of illusions, how to hide feelings. By not allowing Soul growth, the Ego prevents us from experiencing lasting joy and inner peace. We have little hope of real intimacy, for our identity is built upon an illusion."

"But if we don't know this, how can we change it?" I asked.

"Illusions are the sand upon which no structure can be built. The old plans, the old tools and patterns are inadequate and must be discarded. Until one recognizes this and becomes willing to take action, growth at the Soul level cannot occur." Vida gestured with his hands as he spoke.

"So what happens?"

"What happened to you?" Vida moved closer.

"Good question, my friend." I thought for a moment. What had happened to me? I met someone, that's what happened. My life was turned upside down, and I was in a fog. I'd lived for thirty-four years, and I didn't know anything anymore. For the first time in my adult life, I had opened up and let my feelings out. I was a stranger to myself, clueless about the next step. "I screwed up!"

"You made a choice," Vida corrected me.

"A choice?"

"Your choice allowed you to feel."

"Yeah, but Vida, this Hole in the Soul thing you talked about, I am now aware of it, but I don't know how to deal with it." I felt desperate.

"You must trust yourself to your Soul. Although you are unable to comprehend it now, you must let go of what you think will work and listen to the feelings of your Soul. You didn't screw up. You made a choice. That choice led to other choices that have led you here. Remember eighth grade Spanish?"

"What?"

"Eighth grade. You remember Mrs. Rumley's class?" Vida shifted gears quickly.

How could I forget? She had to be the worst teacher I ever had, or so I thought at the time. She was my first Spanish teacher. From the first day of school she talked to our class in Spanish, and I was lost. "I went to see the guidance counselor to try to get out of her class."

"Because?" His eyebrows raised in anticipation of my answer.

"I wasn't learning. I had no idea what she was talking about."

"Because?" He leaned toward me.

"Because it was a foreign language."

"And?" He gestured with his hand.

"The guidance counselor made me stay in that class because Mrs. Rumley's students always learned Spanish better that any other foreign language class. At the end of the semester, I had learned to speak it well."

"So Eric, how are you going to learn about the Hole in your Soul?"

"By staying in the class?"

"Amazing. You may learn yet." He walked toward the door.

"Are you leaving?"

"I'll be back."

"Great," I said in a semi-exasperated tone. What's next? I wondered.

– *Five* –

I FELT LIKE WRITING, SO I FOUND A PIECE OF PAPER AND WROTE SOME thoughts. *The Soul slumbers when we ignore it by denying our feelings. A shipwreck on the ocean floor, it sits, waiting for a current whose power is mighty enough to carry away each of the billions of grains of sand that bind the beast to its grave.*

My Soul slumbered. For years, it laid, waiting for me to wake up and reunite with my Self. I lived as if in a dream, pretending I had it all together. My Ego created a delusional sense of Self. It became an indomitable being who was self-centered and dictatorial. Its paranoid approach to life caused chaos and sheer turmoil in my mind.

My reality was an illusion.

There was a Hole in my Soul. It was where the cold wind blew and the mist of darkness lingered. Over the course of my life, I tried to fill it with alcohol, sex, food, religion, TV, anything. But the Hole kept devouring the futile fixes. There was never enough of anything to fill it. Like a glutenous creature, it was insatiable.

I occasionally isolated myself. Loneliness was my one familiar friend, for even in marriage, my ego held me captive in a jail of my mind where desperation, deceit and despondency were my constant companions.

Filling the Hole became a burden. I tried to apply control to those around me thinking that if everyone would just act and do as I said, my life would be more tolerable. I turned into a dictator, issuing decrees and enforcing them through acts of aggression and outbursts of rage. I was like a savage beast waiting outside his cave for the innocent prey to walk by, attacking with cunning and swiftness and then retreating.

I took hostages in the name of being in love, never knowing or caring what was on the other side of the faces that had become masks of the object of my catharsis. I commanded allegiance and loyalty out of duty to a cause that was lost from its inception.

I continued to write. *Somewhere in the Universe a power moves quietly in the hidden places, a power that sweeps the deep recesses and demolishes the mightiest fortress and conquers the stalwart Ego.*

This same power can fill the Hole in the Soul. It is a power that goes beyond the limits of the human mind and transcends our limited understanding and our elementary ability to grasp that which we choose to call the mystical.

This power is also gentle, considerate and sweet. It distills its simple truths like the dew on the petals of the rose. It waits and works patiently until we have pushed all we can push, pulled all we can pull, and fought all we can fight. And then it can restore our Soul.

A power called Love.

This power found me on that April morning when I was struck down, and placed in this hospital. For some purpose yet to be revealed, I had been ousted from my dictatorial position. I had been brought to a place where I could not make any more choices. Silenced and humbled, I was too weak to make a defense, too wrecked to rebuild with my empty bag of worn-out tools, and too beaten to rally.

I was a whiter shade of pale.

I thought about the rose.

Silly, I thought. How can it be as simple as that? Isn't life more complicated than a rose?

A rose is beautiful, but what happens if it doesn't grow? As I thought more about the rose, I fell asleep and began to dream. An old man appeared dressed in denim bib overalls with a straw hat, frayed and stained dark brown from years of wear and sweat. He had a soft but wrinkled face, and wore a lime green short-sleeved shirt underneath denim overalls and canvas-and-jersey garden gloves soiled with dirt.

He was down on his knees working with a rosebush with his assortment of old, well-used garden tools. It was a hot and humid summer day with the sun overhead, so I guessed it was about noon.

I walked over to the old man.

He must have been expecting me, because without stopping his work he looked over, and said good morning. "You wanna know 'bout roses, huh?" He had a deep southern drawl.

"Well, yes, I suppose so."

"Beautiful flow'r, the purtiest on earth. Takes lots of care. This'n ain't making it, so I'm working on him."

"Why don't you just move it?" I asked.

"That's the last straw. First, I try everythin' else. A rose needs propa sun light, lots of water and soil, so it can live. Weeds can stifle the growth and bugs can, too. If it ain't tended to the rose'll die."

"How do you know what it needs?"

"Don't always. Jus' take a look and see what I see. If there's nothin' at first I get closer and look harder. Like this one. She wasn't getting 'nough water, so I gave her more and still she didn't grow right, so, I checked the soil to see how much acid it had. Then I mixed me some fertilizer to balance it out some. This all helped, but it still isn't comin' 'round quite right.

"So now I gotta look real close at the plant and sure 'nough, - bugs. See?" He pointed to the rose. "So I'm taking care of the little critters now. Only as the last straw, after I've tried everythin' else, will I move a rosebush and replant it. Although, sometimes that's the first thing I do, specially if the soil's too rocky or not the right type for good growin'."

He got up slowly, took an old blue farmer's bandanna out of his back pocket, snapped it open and wiped the sweat from his dirty face. Then in almost one movement, he snapped it down, mashed it up in the same hand and slid the crumbled old rag into his pocket again. "Com' on," he mumbled. "Lemme show you."

I followed him to another section of the garden. I saw every color of rose imaginable. Yellow, pink, red and white. They were radiant in beauty and the fragrance filled the hot summer air. I felt a strange, yet comforting feeling in that part of the garden. It was like being home, secure, warm, peaceful and familiar. The air was slightly different. A soft summer breeze blew gently. It felt refreshing.

The old man must have thought I was crazy. I stood there in awe, mouth open, eyes big as quarters, then I smiled and shook my head. "Wow!" I really know how to wax poetic, I thought.

"Seventy years, out every day workin' on it, always somethin' to do. Sometimes just a lil', sometimes a lot, but always somethin'. Makes me feel real good, fingers dirty, body sweatin', back hurtin', heart poundin', feels real good. Just stand here sometimes. Don't say a word, just stand and look, close my eyes and listen."

"To what?"

He looked at me with that *"You-really-don't-understand,-do-you?"* kind of look that also says *"That's a shame."* The old man answered, "Takes time. Hard work, commitment and desire every day."

I woke up. I must have really been out of it because it took me a few minutes to get myself together, as though my body wasn't quite in synch with my spirit. The dream felt so real I wondered which was reality, the garden or the hospital. After a few moments, I got my bearings. I laid there thinking about the dream and what the old man had said.

"Takes time. Hard work, commitment and desire, every day."

Every day for seventy years, he did something to take care of those beautiful roses. Every day - and he wanted to! He chose to!

Vida said that being open was like a rose; it allows your true beauty to be seen. The old man said that to keep roses beautiful, you had to work every day, and that it should be a choice, not a duty.

But the ground? What was my ground? Could I become open in my current "soil?"

"Time for lunch, Mr. Crane." I was startled as the nurse came into the room. "Been sleeping? You must be tired!"

"I suppose I am, at that!" Come to think of it, I was not sure when I was awake and when I had drifted off to sleep. I guess I was tired. And what was the main course? I removed the stainless steel plate cover. Mystery Meat smothered in gravy! I hadn't had mystery meat since the Marines! With food like that, who wanted to go home!

The phone rang. I reached over and picked up the receiver. "Hello?"

"Hi, Honey." It was Sonnie. "I just got the kids taken care of, and I'm getting ready to come over. I should be there in about an hour or so."

Sonnie never was definitive about a time. An hour or so usually meant more "or so" than an hour.

"Okay. Hey, would you mind bringing me a spiral notebook?"

"A spiral notebook?"

"Yeah, I've written some stuff and want to do more. You can get one at the drug store."

"Sure, sure. Okay, well, in that case I may be a couple of hours. I guess I'll see you when I see you."

"Okay, see you later." I hung up the phone and ate lunch.

— *Six* —

After lunch, I went back in my mind to January of '88. It was a blustery cold winter day in Spokane. Six inches of snow had fallen the night before onto the already icy streets. I made my way slowly to the office along the winding Spokane streets, listening to the traffic and weather reports on the local AM radio station. I drove into the parking garage, gave the attendant my keys, grabbed my briefcase and walked out to the sidewalk. The street plows had been through hours before and had piled the snow into three-foot banks in the street gutter. Thank God for rubber shoe covers. I kept a spare pair in my trunk, and on occasions like that, I was plenty glad I did. The sidewalks had been shoveled, not by hand, but with a snow blower. According to the tire tracks, it must have been a large blower. Ice melting pellets had been thrown along the sidewalks in front of the stores, but it was not enough for the amount of ice and snow on that twenty-one degree Spokane morning. Carefully I made my way to the street corner, waited for the light to change and stepped into the street sludge and snow. When I reached the other side, I quickly headed for the revolving doors to the Paulsen Building. It used to house doctors only, but with the flight of doctors to the 'burbs, the old building had been renovated for general office use. We had our office on the twelfth floor, so everyone who worked at Systech took the elevator.

The elevator doors opened, and I stepped inside with six others. Two ladies, who appeared like they were in their late forties, stood in front of me, talking about how bad the roads had been. An older gentleman, to my left, appeared like he might be a doctor. We stopped at the third floor and a young woman left for her office, then at the fifth floor, where the gentleman exited. On to the ninth, then the tenth, and finally it was my turn to exit on the twelfth floor. The elevator doors opened into our executive lobby, an impressive high tech waiting area with clear plate glass walls revealing the executive conference room behind the mahogany reception area.

"Good morning, Eric." Lucy, the Systech receptionist, greeted me with her exceptionally pleasant tone.

"Hello there, Lucy. Got here early, huh?" Lucy was always there by seven-twenty and always had a bright smile.

I made my way to my office, and it seemed as though it was just any other day. Donna was not there yet, but that was normal, because I got in at seven-thirty and the office did not open until eight-thirty.

Donna and I were by then in full affair mode. After Christmas my cravings of being with her increased. Despite my best efforts at denying my desire to be with her, I finally succumbed. The heat of love's passion had climbed to an inferno, and making love had taken on a new dimension. I could not get enough, yet at the same time, pangs of guilt racked my gut. I was married to Michele, but all I wanted was Donna.

I was considering what I should do about my marriage, about Donna, about living at home versus moving out. My mind was spun at five thousand rpms like a steely marble in a stainless steel bowl. Should I stay with Michele, or should I move out? I knew I was not going to move in with Donna. She had not asked, and I knew it was wrong to do so.

I couldn't believe what I was thinking, but nonetheless it was all I could think about. I was insistent about getting out of the house, and being with Donna.

Someone tapped on my office door frame. I looked up to see Rich, my boss and friend. His face wore a tired look of defeat, as though he had lost his house in an all night poker game. "Got a minute?"

"Sure!" I glanced at my watch. Eight-fifteen. I had spent almost an hour thinking about my dilemma.

"The board is meeting today to discuss some major issues." Rich's tone was grave.

"Oh?" A pang of fear rushed through me.

"It doesn't look good for you."

"What do you mean?" A dark sinking feeling developed in the pit of my gut.

"Some jobs are going to be eliminated and all unnecessary positions are being reviewed." Rich had difficulty maintaining eye contact.

"That good, huh?" I faked a smile, thinking it could change things.

"I'll keep you informed." He walked out.

I swirled around in my executive chair and looked out the windows into the gray Spokane winter morning. I switched my thinking immediately. Unnecessary positions? Not me. After all, I was responsible for more revenue generation than any of the other sales people. But who was I kidding? I sank into despair as I feared the worst. What if I lost my job? How would I support the family? What would I do? Scratch moving out! I'd call Michele, no, call Donna first, no ... no better call Michele first. But what would I say? "I'm not going to move out because I might lose my job."? That didn't sound right. Maybe I should call Donna first and talk to her about it, I thought. But she wouldn't be home. She was either at work, or on her way. "Just wait a few minutes, Crane," I told myself. I tried to find something to do while I waited to talk to her. There was an expense report in my brief-case I had not completed. I finished it, and submitted it for approval. Then I called Donna. "I have to speak to you now. It's urgent."

"Well, good morning to you too." Hearing her voice calmed me slightly.

"Sorry," I paused, "but I really need to talk. Got a few minutes?"

"Sure. Downstairs," she replied.

We found a table in the back corner of the coffee bar, off the main lobby, that was out of sight of passers-by. She listened to me pontificate about how valuable I was to the company, how no one could match my revenue contribution over the past two quarters. She merely listened. She held my hand and listened until I finished.

Then she spoke. "While you were on your last trip there was an executive management meeting. Lee Finwald has somehow managed to shift the power base, and now he has a lot of influence on the board."

"That's okay, I'm aligned with Jim, Rich and Hank." Jim was the Chairman and CEO. Rich and Hank were the co-founders. "They like me. Hell they hired me! They won't let me go. Maybe they will let Scott and Russ go, but not me."

"Just be careful. Finwald doesn't like you," warned Donna.

"Just because I told the guy to get screwed in a management meeting? Can't he take a joke?" We finished our coffee, said good-bye and left separately.

That whole day I attempted to make myself as visible as possible to top management. Every time they took a break I was in the halls looking busier than ever. I was working this deal, solving that problem, putting together some 'big' report and meeting with my team.

At the end of the day Rich, called me to his office. I closed the door behind me and took a seat against the wall. Rich's desk faced the window so nothing was between him and the person with whom he was talking.

I thought I'd lead with a positive statement. "Must have been some meeting!"

"It sure was," replied Rich, who looked hammered. "I don't know how all this happened but they are firing Jim, Hank and me."

"What? They can't fire you guys! You're the company! How can they do that?"

"They own the stock now, that's how." His voice was a mixture of anger and regret.

Two years before Rich and Hank sought some venture capital to grow the business. They hired Jim as president, because he had an impressive track record growing the revenues of another high-tech company. Eventually, the venture capitalists acquired enough stock and had enough seats on the board of directors to control the company. The company had not been performing according to plans, so the venture capitalists fired the guys at the top.

"Now, about you. It was determined that your position was not essential to the core business of the company and that you ..."

My instant thought came midstream in Rich's sentence, "Not essential! NOT ESSENTIAL! TO WHOM?"

" ... can continue on straight commission, or you can leave and look elsewhere. I'm sorry, Eric, but it's not personal, it's strictly business." His head hung low.

My thought was sarcastic, *"Yeah, right."* My words, on the other hand, were polite. "I understand Rich, it's business."

I left his office with a nauseated feeling. I walked as calmly as possible to my office across the open area. It was only a twenty-foot walk, but it might as well have been a mile. I faked a smile as I walked in slow motion, past the other office workers who I felt were watching my every step. I stuffed my feelings down as deep as I could, the way I did when I was beaten as a child. I needed fresh air.

I went into my office, grabbed my coat and took the stairs down twelve floors. My walk was mechanical, as if I were marching to a death drum. I remembered back when Kennedy was buried, how eerie the drums sounded during the funeral procession. I pushed the heavy glass doors open into the Arctic chill, the wind cutting through all I wore. With my head down, as if I were looking for pennies on the sidewalk, I went out to the streets to the first bar I could find, sat at a stool and ordered a rum and Coke, and another, and another and another. It was 5:35 p.m. and that was my first drink in thirteen years. So much for abstinence.

Sonnie walked through my hospital door. "Hi, Honey, how are you?" she asked.

"Hey, baby." I quickly returned my thoughts to the present.

She came over and gave me a small kiss on my cheek, as I sat up in the bed.

"Here's a notebook. What are you writing?" She handed me the pad, walked over to the chair and sat down.

"It's fascinating. Abliel and Vida are teaching me a lot about love, I'm also thinking about my life, especially about Spokane." I paused, looked over at the window and continued. "I've had extraordinary dreams and Vida's helping me understand their message to me. He's teaching me about life, and I really want to get it written down."

"Wow! That's fascinating." She looked at me as if I were sort of weird, yet I suppose somehow she knew what I was saying was real.

"I know it sounds a bit off the wall, but I swear, Sonnie, something is going on here that I can't fully explain."

"That's okay. Is there any real need to discuss it now?"

"I suppose not, but I feel it's important to write about it. Something is pushing me to get it down on paper. I have a high sense of urgency."

"Then write! I'm sure it will help," she encouraged.

I wondered if she was truly getting it, or was she simply making conversation. I decided to change the topic. "How are the kids?"

"They're fine." She rambled on about what had been happening at home, while I wondered if she would ever be able to understand what was happening to me. Maybe she no longer cared. She talked for a few more minutes and gathered her things. "Well, I guess its time for me to go. I told the baby sitter I would only be an hour or so." In other words, she would be gone for the rest of the afternoon, I thought.

"Thanks for the notebook." I uttered as she got up and walked to my bed.

"You're welcome, Honey." She leaned over the bed and gave me a kiss on my cheek, turned and walked toward the door.

"See you later," I said as she stopped, turned back and blew me a kiss.

– *Seven* –

BACK TO SPOKANE. I HAD TAKEN A DRINK, WELL ACTUALLY I HAD A LOT
of drinks. I don't recall getting home, but the next morning I felt awful
and called in sick. When I finally stumbled out of bed, it was long after
the kids had left for school. I found the kitchen and ate toast and
drank some Seven-Up. I was hung over, had a dry mouth and a head
that was about to split open. Sweat poured down my face. Michele was
out doing something at the church. The house was quiet and empty,
and I had some time to think, however, my brain wasn't working right.
I had no thoughts other than fleeting ones. If I could slow it down, I
could figure a way out of this jam. But I came up snake eyes. Nothing.
Nada. Zip.

My thoughts were like an out-of-control range fire. "Michele,
Donna, kids, home, job, no job, I'm no good, I'm a failure, it's no use.
Why me? Poor me! Nobody understands me." And feelings? I had
feelings all right. I was so angry at Lee Finwald and the venture capitalists that I couldn't think of anything except revenge. I was about
to explode!

So I did. I went outside into the cold winter snow and let it out. I
cursed God. I had devoted my whole life to the church and had given
ten percent and more of my gross income and had done everything the
church had asked of me, yet my life was miserable and falling apart!

I cursed God with vile and crude words. It was His fault! I did what
I was supposed to, it was His fault things weren't working out. The

church had always taught me that if I kept the commandments, everything would turn out okay and I would know happiness and peace.

But things had not turned out okay. My life was in turmoil and my mind was sprinting to insanity. Someone was to blame. Someone must always take the blame. God was to blame!

A few minutes later, I finished screaming, yelling and cursing. I went inside and sat by the big iron wood-stove. I sat in "my" chair. My big reddish brown recliner where I watched football, basketball and baseball games.

I had insidious thoughts of revenge, self pity, fear, panic and then more revenge. Round in circles I went, eventually spiraling down, out of control. I sank deeper and deeper and felt like a failure.

After about an hour, I thought about a distributor of mine in Atlanta. The owner knew me and knew of my experience in the software business. I wanted to call him to explore opportunities. In my mind, I rehearsed what I would say. I paced the floor while my brain went into overdrive. I had to call him now, but I had to not appear desperate. I'd be my old self, and put on the charm and act like everything was normal. I found the phone, dialed his number and waited.

"Thank you for calling The Affiliated Group. May I help you?" A pleasant female voice answered.

"Frank Grimes, please."

I was put on hold. Country music. Frank liked country music. I listened. "Take this job and shove it, I ain't workin' here no more..."

"Frank Grimes."

"Frank, this is Eric Crane. How are you?"

"Hey Eric, good to hear from you. What's new?"

"Well, there was a board meeting yesterday, and Rich, Hank, Jim and I got fired." I blurted the news quickly.

"You're kidding!" Frank's tone was incredulous.

"Nope. Just like that they cleaned house."

"I thought you were doing some good things."

"I am, or, was. I guess I was on the wrong political team. Lee Finwald and his guys are going to remain there."

"That's incredible, Eric. You never know with a gang like that. Get a group of venture capital companies on the board, and strange things are bound to happen. So what are you going to do?"

"I have no idea at this point, it's all so fresh. I could stay on and work straight commission, which may not be all bad. I thought I'd call you and get a fresh perspective."

"I'm glad you did. You know, things are really growing here. Why don't you come out and talk with me? I sure could use some help."

Yes! Sevens!

"That sounds great, Frank. What's a good time for you?"

"Next week's good Eric. I'll be in Greensboro this week, but next weekend is open. How about I have Carrie make the arrangements, if that's okay with you?"

"Sounds like a plan. Let's do it!"

When Michele came home, I described to her the events of the day before. She sat and listened. I watched her face change as I said I had been fired. I may as well have told her someone in the family had died. Her face showed horror and panic as she looked out the living room window to the snow-covered forest that surrounded the house.

"What are we going to do?" Her voice was solemn.

"I'm going to Atlanta next week to discuss an opportunity with Frank Grimes."

"Atlanta? But that's so far away!"

"It's where I need to go for now." That was that. The king had spoken. Michele knew not to rebut when my tone was patriarchal.

The following week I boarded the plane to Atlanta. I was feeling scared. I ordered a scotch as soon as I was seated. That's the benefit of flying first class, free drinks. During the flight, I must have drunk too many, because by the time I got to Atlanta, I was loaded.

Somehow, I got to the hotel. It was a luxurious hotel in mid-town Atlanta. I checked in, changed clothes, got a bottle from the mini-bar and headed out for the night.

I had read in the airplane magazine of a great blues club in Atlanta, so I made my way over to Blues Harbor. It rocked. A real blues joint with black brick walls, a black ceiling and red and blue lights scattered about. Thin wisps of cigarette smoke floated above the mellow crowd. At the table in front of me was a young black couple, whispering in each other's ear, giggling and enjoying a bottle of wine. Across the other side of the joint was a table of what looked like conventioneers. They were all drunk and having a great time. Over in the corner opposite the door was a small stage where all of a sudden I heard a guitar wail out a familiar blues riff.

The spotlight shone on a short, fat, white guy with black sunglasses and a black hat, like the Blues Brothers wore. He had long blonde hair hanging down his back and a bushy beard down to his chest and a Strat slung over his pot belly. He had his Peavey Classic Fifty amp cranked up and was laying down an old Elmore James tune like I never heard it laid down before. Man, that guy was cookin'! I sat down at the bar next to a reasonably attractive woman, ordered a double and started singing with him. For that one night, Dr. Dewars, a girl at the bar named Sandra, Guitar Gary and the Bluesmen made me feel like I had died and gone to heaven. After the show was over, Sandra and I went to her place and partied the rest of the night away.

The next day was Saturday and Frank and I met at nine o'clock at his office. His company was experiencing tremendous growth, so I was quite interested in knowing why.

"Hey, Eric! How's Atlanta so far?" Frank asked smiling.

"Hey" is the word people in Georgia use for "Hi" or "Hello". Frank had lived in the South most of his adult life, and anyone who lived in Georgia for more than a week soon said "Hey" and "ya'll".

"Morning, Frank. Can't complain. I'm going to like it here."

"How about some coffee?" He had brewed a fresh pot earlier.

"Perfect. Black for me."

"So, you like Atlanta?" He filled my mug and handed it over to me.

"So far, so good." I grabbed a napkin to pick up any spills for the walk to Frank's office.

"I'm glad you're here, Eric. We've been going real strong lately, and I could sure use some help." He described what he needed in some detail, someone who could put a deal together and then manage the account for the long-term relationship. "Interested?"

I hadn't expected him to cut to the chase so quickly. I was more accustomed to political business chat, wherein you use ten minutes of fluff, hype and BS to make a one-sentence point.

"Sure! What have you got in mind?" I tried not to sound too eager.

"You mean your compensation package?"

"Yeah," I was apprehensive.

"Name it." He sat back in his chair, arms fanned out.

I couldn't believe my ears! He was offering me the chance to write my own ticket! I laid it out in front of him, and we put together a deal. The rest of the morning was spent reviewing the business plan and the existing customer accounts. After lunch, he had some errands to run and I searched for an apartment. The newspaper had a fairly large apartment section, that I went through while downing a sub sandwich. A specific one stood out from the rest.

> Executive apartment in a private
> home, furnished. Deposit/first &
> last. References Call 555-4628

I called, got directions and drove right over. The downstairs suite had been built in from the basement. The front part of the divided room had a small refrigerator, microwave, sink, couch, TV and easy chair. Behind the divider was a double bed, matching dresser and a closet. A bathroom with a shower and a small vanity, was located adjacent to the bedroom. It even had its own towels. I gave the owners a deposit and the required rent, walked out to the car to get my suitcase, walked back in and unpacked. I had a new home.

I went back to Spokane on Monday and made arrangements to move to Atlanta.

Michele was not too happy about leaving Spokane. She had obviously been thinking about things between us, because the first thing she said was: "Eric, what happens if we get there and then we get divorced? Then what?"

It hit me unexpectedly. We had not discussed divorce, yet, here it was.

"I don't know. Suppose we do, and suppose we don't? That's not my concern right now. I've got to have a job, and this is a job. If you don't want to move to Atlanta, then fine. Stay here!" In my usual macho fashion, I had escalated the stakes to a take-it-or-leave-it deal. Unsympathetic to her thoughts and feelings, I had made plans, and I was going to carry them through. Anger started to swell. I was unemployed, had a family, a mortgage, bills and here before me lay the solution. Why couldn't she see that? She had no appreciation for the devastating feeling a man has when he has no job. She could not possibly feel the pressure to keep things afloat during a crisis, like I felt. I was good at assuming what Michele felt and did not feel. Wrapped up in my feelings only, and looking at matters from my perspective, my anger continued to grow.

"It's a job and it's in Atlanta, and I'm taking it. That's all I know. If you want to stay here, then fine. Stay here." Engulfed in rage, I stormed out of the room and into the garage, started the car, slammed it into reverse and drove off, cursing the whole situation. Why couldn't Michele see what I was trying to do for the family? How ungrateful of her.

The speedometer was up to sixty-five, and I was in a forty-five mph zone, going around curves on a two lane road that cut through the forests north of Spokane. I was going nowhere, but hell bent on getting there. I was in a blind rage and there was no telling where I was headed, or why. I was in motion, running away. From what? I had no idea, but I was running, nonetheless. Finally, it dawned on me to go see Donna.

I slowed the car down, and pulled over at a gas station to use the phone. I threw a quarter in the slot and punched in her number. Busy. Just my luck. I walked over to the station, bought a beer, took a swig and went back to the pay phone, slammed in another quarter and beat the number buttons again. "Damn," still busy. I figured I'd drive over and surprise her, so I turned the car around and headed back toward town.

Never try to get anywhere quickly in Spokane. The sadistic traffic engineers played a cruel joke on the city the way they designed the road system and the traffic lights. There is no such thing as making two lights in a row, and the speed limit is only twenty-five. Perhaps the traffic department was in bed with the police department, and speeding tickets paid for the road system, which was always in repair, somewhere. That day, it was in a state of repair all the way to Donna's house, so by the time I got there, I was really miffed.

I walked up to the porch, rang the doorbell and looked inside through the beveled glass on either side of the door. Donna jumped up from the couch, pulled down her sweatshirt and pulled up her jeans. Some guy stuck his head up to look over to the door to see who was there. I froze.

Donna came to the door, opened it and with a very surprised look on her face said, "Eric, I didn't expect you. you should have called first."

"I tried. Guess I'll leave." I started to turn away.

"No, don't. Please I -"

"No, Donna really, not now, not today, I'll see ya." I completed my turn and walked away. Stunned by what I had seen, I found my car, cranked it up and pulled off. The tears started, but I fought them back. "Hell no, Crane, it's not worth it." I found the nearest store, bought a six-pack of beer and drove to nowhere, but someplace, anyplace where I could numb out and not feel it. I found it on the north side of town. I drove until tears blurred my vision to the extent I couldn't see, pulled over, got out and yelled. I yelled loud and long.

Sunday morning arrived and I held tickets for the one o'clock flight to Atlanta that afternoon. It was six-thirty and I was severely hung over, but I got up, because it was my last day with my children. I fixed breakfast, something I did regularly on weekends because the kids loved the way I scrambled eggs. I learned it from my grandmother. She knew how to make the best breakfast in Richmond, so I used her recipe for the children on the weekends, per their request.

They ate a half dozen eggs at a sitting. We finished breakfast with toast and strawberry jam. Michele took them to church while I tried to get over my relentless hangover and packed for Atlanta. Two suitcases, a briefcase and a garment bag were packed tight. A book or two and some silverware wrapped in a bath towel were thrown in. I grabbed a few pictures of the children and carefully slid them in some folded sheets. In one of the pictures, the kids were dressed in the matching blue T-shirts I had bought for them in New Orleans a few years earlier. It was my favorite.

They got home around noon, with enough time for the twenty-minute ride to the airport. Michele drove. I spent the time talking to the children.

"What's Atlanta like, Daddy?"

"Do they have schools there?"

"Can I take my friends?"

"Do they have a lot of snow there?"

Art Linkletter used to say "Kids say the darndest things!" Mine were no exception.

We got to the airport, and the children didn't know what to say. They knew I was leaving for a city that was far away. How distant, they did not know, but they knew it was a long way, because I had to fly there. I sometimes think children know a lot more than we give them credit for knowing. They knew something was up. Something inside them must have said, "Your Daddy is leaving for good." They started to cry. I had flown away on business at least a hundred times in the past, but this was the only time they cried. No, they sobbed. Standing on the sidewalk, I hugged each one and tried as best I could to hold back my own tears. Michele sat in the drivers seat waiting for it all to end. One by one I hugged and kissed each child and told them how much I loved them and that I would see them again soon. They got back into the van. The tears flowed and their small bodies shook uncontrollably. Michele drove off. I watched them waving good-bye from the back window of the van until they were out of sight. Tears streamed from behind my sunglasses. I picked up my bags, walked inside and found the bar. A quick double shot of scotch, and I was ready for the airplane.

When we took off I quietly said, "Good-bye kids. Good-bye Michele."

I didn't want to say the next good-bye. I was scared that if I did, I would never find another connected relationship again. I was afraid, but I felt more hurt, from seeing her with another man, than fear, so I finally said, "Good-bye, Donna."

There I said it. The affair with Donna had been hot, quick and short-lived. I spent the flight drinking and thinking, trying to figure out how I could undo the past and dreading the thought of living alone in the future. And my children? The guilt felt terrible. The scotch couldn't work quickly enough, so I ordered six more bottles. The flight attendant said she couldn't give me that much at one time, so I got three, drank them, and ordered three more from another flight attendant when we were over Kansas.

On landing, I took a limo to the apartment, by the way of the liquor store, finished off a pint and passed out on the sofa.

Monday mornings are an unwelcome interruption to an otherwise good weekend. That Monday was especially unwelcome. With a throbbing head and a dry mouth, I rolled out of bed and stumbled to the shower. The apartment was so small that the steam from the shower filled the place, covering each of the two windows like a cloud. After a quick shave, a token tooth brushing and a swig of mouthwash, I found my cleanest wrinkled shirt, a dark suit, a pair of dark socks and a maroon-and-navy-striped tie, brushed my hair and struck out for the office, stopping by McDonalds for coffee.

I met Frank at the office, and we reviewed customer accounts. The company had a minor cash flow crunch and my first job was to see what money I could collect. I began calling customers to introduce myself and to ask for payments. When I looked up for air, it was three-thirty and I had worked through lunch, oblivious to everyone else in the office. I found that immersing myself in work was a good way to not feel any of the other issues that were going on with me at the time. I could forget about the other problems in my life when I was at work, and because I had no family to go home to, I worked all day and all night, every day. I avoided dealing with anything other than work, although somedays, it wasn't that easy. As hard as I worked, the loneliness was still there, waiting patiently for me to get back to the apartment, so it could pounce upon my mind and gnaw at my guts. When I finally did leave the office, I went out to eat and got drunk or I stayed home and ate a microwaved dinner and got drunk. Either way, I tried to get rid of that hollow, dark place inside. It had no name, but it had taken residency in me, and when it howled, I ached; when I ached, I either drank or forced myself to work harder and longer.

My phone rang. It was Michele.

"Eric?" Her voice told me something was wrong.

"Yeah?"

"I need to talk to you. Have you got just a minute?"

"Sure, I guess so, what's the matter?"

"Erica fell and broke her arm. She's okay but she wanted me to call you so she could tell you herself. Can you talk to her?"

"Sure, but what happened?"

"Oh, she was running outside through the woods and tripped on a fallen pine and evidently fell the wrong way on her arm, but she wants to tell you, so I'll put her on."

"Daddy?" I hadn't heard Erica's voice for a few weeks. She sounded like she had been crying.

"Yes, Pumpkin?" I called her by her nickname.

"Daddy, I broke my arm, and I want you to come home so I can see you."

My button had been pushed. The guilt in my gut moved. Reaction. What to do? No time to think, go with instinct. "You do? Well, tell me about how you broke it." That bought a few minutes while she told me her story. I figured if I could keep her talking, I could respond without losing it. I wanted to see the children, but this wasn't the right time. We were at the end of a quarter and I had to book all the revenue I could, and collect as much cash as possible, so the bank would get off our backs about the line of credit.

"Gosh, Pumpkin, that sounds awful. How was the trip to the doctor, were you scared?" Wrong question, Crane.

"Yes, and that's why I want you to come home, Daddy. I miss you, and I'm sad without you here." She sniffled.

"I miss you too, Pumpkin, and I wish I could be there, but I can't, right now. How about if I check to see when I could come see you? And I'll call you back tomorrow. Will that be okay?"

"Yeah," sob, "but I love you, Daddy."

"I love you so much, Pumpkin. You just put a smile on your pretty little face, because everything is going to be okay. You'll see. Can I talk to your mom, now?"

"Okay. Good-bye, Daddy."

"Good-bye, Erica."

Michele got on the line. "Yes?"

"Uh, I told her I would check on flight schedules and call her back tomorrow. What do things look like on your end?"

"Well, you can come whenever. The kids really miss you and want to see you real bad," she implored.

"Okay, I'll check it out and call back tomorrow. Okay?"

"All right. I guess I'll talk to you then." She was cold.

"Okay. Bye." Guilt ridden, I had to get off the phone.

"Good-bye, Eric." Ice cold.

I hung up and stared out the window that overlooked the parking lot. I wasn't really looking at anything, I was trying to sort out my thoughts. Erica had pulled my heartstrings, and I was feeling pain from guilt and feelings I had tried to believe weren't there by ignoring them. I must not have been doing a very good job, because my eyes got wet and tears started to fall down my face. I quickly grabbed my handkerchief and wiped them away. "Better get out of here, Crane." I thought, because I felt the throes of guilt rumble inside. I grabbed my briefcase, put on my suit coat and headed for the door.

"Tell Frank something's come up at home, and I'll call him

tonight." I blurted out to Carrie, as I walked quickly past her desk, keeping my eyes fixed on anything but another human being.

I made it to the car, unlocked the door and sat in the driver's seat, put the key in the ignition and cranked it. I sat still, and it happened. My stomach rolled and a feeling made its way to my throat. I opened my mouth and screamed, letting out the excrutiating pain from the guilt I felt from being away from my children. It was as if someone had stuck a machete in my gut and was twisting it around, destroying everything in its path. I howled with my eyes closed, curled up in pain. I needed help, and I needed it immediately.

During my last session with Amy, I had been given the name of a therapist in Atlanta. She had written it on one of her business cards. I reached in my left rear pants pocket, pulled out my leather wallet and picked out all the business cards. Amy's was next to last. There it was, Hans Deitrich.

I picked up the car phone and dialed.

"Goot afternoon, theese ees Hans." His eastern European accent was thick.

"Hans, my name is Crane, Eric Crane, and, uh, I got your name from Amy Carlson in Spokane, Washington. I'm new here in Atlanta, and I need help."

"Vhat kind of help do you need, Eric?"

"I would like to see you, today; in fact, this afternoon, if it's possible? Is it?"

"Let me see, Eric, dis afternoon you say? How about five o'clock? Is dis okay vith you?"

"Yes, this, uh, that's okay. Where are you?"

He gave me directions that I scribbled on the back of an envelope I found in the passenger seat. I had not been in Atlanta long enough to know that his office was an hour away in rush hour traffic and it was almost four o'clock already. I put the car in gear and drove off, to see Hans.

I found his office and let myself in through his office door. There was no receptionist.

"Hello? I'm here!" I looked around for a person.

"Be vith you in a minute. Please, take a seat," came a voice from somewhere.

I sat down in the one chair in the waiting area. By then I had gotten myself back together, but barely. Hans came out to greet me.

"Ah, Eric, good to meet you. Please, come in here."

Han's thick German accent made him difficult to understand. I went into his counseling room, which had no chairs at all in it. Several bean bag chairs sat on the floor, a box of tissues between two of them. In the corner was a brown teddy bear. I took a seat on one of the bean bags.

"Eric, vhy are you here?"

"For therapy, of course."

"Vhat do you feel?"

Oh no, here we go again. Feelings. Maybe I had made a mistake in coming to see this guy. "Nothing." I thought I had him.

"Vhat does nothing feel like?"

I knew this wasn't going to be easy, but it was costing me money, so I figured I better go with it. "I don't know...like a glob I guess."

"Vhat is glob?"

"A glob, you know."

"Do you like dis glob?"

"Come on..."

Silence. He had direct eye contact with me and said nothing.

"No, I don't like this glob."

"Then vhat do you vant to do with it, Eric?"

"Get rid of it?"

"So, you feel like zee glob and you vant to get rid of it. Vhat are you going to do with it."

I looked at him, because I didn't understand. Did he say "what am I going to do with it?" I wondered. "That's why I'm here. I want you to tell me what to do with it."

"Tell me Eric, if you had glob here, vhat would you do with it?"

"I would flush it!"

"So, Eric, vhy don't you flush it!"

Flush it? Crane, you've really picked one this time, I told myself. You picked a therapist you can't understand, you're talking about a glob, and now he wants you to flush it! I pretended to throw the glob in a toilet and grabbed for the handle to flush it.

"No, no Eric, look at zee glob first. Vhat is it?"

Oh well, I thought, what have I got to lose? "Just a glob."

"Be zee glob, Eric."

"What?" I could not understand his instruction.

"Be zee glob. If you were zee glob, what would you say?"

I thought, "Be the glob. Okay, I'm the glob." I sat there.

"Vhere are you, Eric?"

"I'm being the glob." I felt stupid.

"Vhat do you feel?"

"Feel? Like a glob!" I paused.

Hans looked me in the eyes, said nothing, only stared.

I sat there and looked down at the carpet, and then ... then I felt something. Something deep within me. Way down inside something shifted and moved. It shifted slightly in my soul and stirred like a monster of the nautical deep.

Hans must have noticed, because I could hear him say "Yeah, schtay vith it Eric," in a coach-like way.

Slowly and then slightly, ever so slightly, it moved up. I could feel it move within as it lumbered from my loins to my gut up to my chest and then my throat. Then it stopped.

"Schtay vith it."

My throat tightened like someone was choking me.

The feeling stuck in my throat. It was close.

"Yeah, good, let it out, Eric. It's okay. Let it all out!"

It got bigger and pushed harder until it filled me, and then I opened my mouth and it came out.

"AAAAAAAAAAAAHHHHHHHHHHHHHHHHHHH!!!!!!!!!!!!!!!!!"

"Yea, dat's it Eric, be zee glob!"

"AAAAAAAAAAAAHHHHHHHHHHHHHHHHHHHHHH!!!!!!!!!!!!!!!!!"

I howled as loud as I could for, as long as I could. From deep within my belly came a primal, blood curdling sound, so wretched, violent and terrifying that I shook with fear. It demanded to come out. I cried as I released it. I sobbed and screamed as I let it out. As loud as I could, it continued to come out, until I was finally exhausted. When it was over, I collapsed on the floor.

Hans brought me back to the present moment and helped me regain my composure. "It's all right, Eric." He gave me some tissues. I sat there for a moment. The demon had been released. Hans told me that was enough for one day. We stood up, hugged and I left.

I had felt something, again.

As I lay there in the hospital bed, the nurse interrupted my memories. "Time for your vitals check again, Mr. Crane."

The day had passed quickly, and now the evening nurse had arrived. As she put a thermometer in my mouth, I noticed an angel pin on her collar.

She continued to check my blood pressure and take my pulse. "Okay, everything is fine. See you later." She walked out and I laid there.

"Abliel, this stuff is coming up so fast."

"Its okay Eric. Continue to recall. You need to see how you were. You need to know that you were closed up, and it's important that you discover how to open your heart to experience Love."

"But, the memories are painful!"

"The ways of your past must be overcome, so you can move forward."

"But why can't it be forgotten?"

"Yesterday is only important in the lessons we learn from it. You will not repeat lessons that you successfully learn."

"I don't want to repeat any of them."

"The choices you made then, do not have to be made in the present, if you learned from them."

I wondered if I had, in fact, learned from them.

"Get your rest, and remember, pure Love needs a new creation for it to find its expression in you."

"Thanks, my friend." I closed my eyes and thought this whole thing was too bizarre.

– *Eight* –

I THOUGHT BACK ABOUT MY EARLY DAYS IN ATLANTA. SEVERAL MONTHS had passed since I last saw my children. The pain of being separated from them was greater than I anticipated. I don't know what I expected really, but it was extremely difficult, to say the least. At night, I drank several glasses of scotch and cried myself to sleep. I often worked from seven in the morning until ten at night, simply to keep my mind busy so I wouldn't have to think about the separation. On the real lonely nights, I got my old Fender guitar out of its case and sang the blues. There's something about singing the blues when you're feeling bad that makes life a little more tolerable, especially when you're drunk, and I was surely drunk.

I wondered if I was doing the right thing by leaving Spokane. Was that much pain worth it? Maybe I could go back and try harder, or maybe I was just sinful and needed to repent. My feelings and thoughts were often confused. Rather than deal with them, I blocked them with work or numbed them with scotch.

My business trips took me to southeastern cities like Nashville, Memphis, Richmond, Raleigh, Charlotte, Tampa and Orlando. One of my favorites was Birmingham. I like the rolling hills and the friendly people there. I stayed at the Prestwick Hotel in the Five Points district of downtown Birmingham. The Prestwick is a quaint old hotel, remodeled and refurbished in a delightful elegant southern manner, that gives it class. There was a small bar where one could go for a drink and some quiet thoughts.

Next door was a trendy restaurant that brewed its own beer and offered seven different brews. I couldn't make up my mind, so I had the waitress bring me one of each. The first round was so good, I ordered another. I thought about my children and my heart sank to the floor. I ordered a scotch and tried to put the thought away, but it wouldn't go. I paid the check and went for a walk.

An old church sat across the street from the restaurant. I strolled around the sacred edifice and marveled at the craftsmanship. I thought, "it's a shame that they don't build buildings like they used to." The foundation was made of hand cut stone. The walls were brick, and the windows were trimmed in stone. Seven stained glass windows adorned each side, but since it was dark, I couldn't see what they were. I wondered why everyone was in such a hurry to build things today that they wouldn't take the time to make it nice and reflective of the craftsmanship of the tradesmen. I must not have paid attention to the time, because when I looked around everyone had disappeared from the street. A quick glance at my watch told me it was one o'clock. I had a morning meeting that started at seven-thirty! Quickly, I walked back to the room, requested a six-thirty wake up call, and fell asleep.

The night nurse walked in, interrupting my memories. "Time to turn out the lights, Mr. Crane",

"Okay, just a few more minutes?"

"Just a few." The nurses were friendly, after all, this was a hospital, so why shouldn't they have been?

I had to write my last recollections down. Just a few more sentences, then it was time for sleep, "as if you haven't slept all day," I thought. I pulled the cord that turned out the lights.

I fell asleep and soon was dreaming again. I was in a dark and cold cave where I heard water trickling in the distance. Although I was standing upright, I couldn't move much. I looked down to my ankles and saw a big black cast iron chain around my right ankle with a three-inch shackle and a rusty black padlock.

My face was drawn and pale, dark circles lined my eyes. My expression bore fear and anxiety. My hair was long and uncombed, and my beard was stringy and long. My ribs showed through my bare body. It was as if I were a hundred years old.

Another presence seemed to be in the cave. It felt dark and terrible, like an unseen monster with foul odor and heavy labored breathing. The monster was going to get me. I needed to escape, but how?

I looked for a key to open the padlock, but my search was in vain. Finally I gave up and dropped my hand to my side. When I relaxed my grip, I discovered the key was in the palm of my hand. As my hands trembled with fear, I frantically opened the padlock. The monster was close. I felt its warm breath on my neck. Then, as its hand grabbed my shoulder, I let out a shrill scream.

The being took me into both of his hands and turned me toward him. I shut my eyes, so I wouldn't see. He held me, and whimpered. I opened my right eye slowly. Nothing happened. I opened my left eye. I couldn't believe it! The monster looked like King Kong.

He was a gorilla, but his eyes looked human. I looked into his eyes, his deep brown eyes. They were exactly like mine! He felt familiar to me, strange as that might seem, like someone I had once known, but had long since forgotten. A voice sounded in my mind.

"He's you."

I looked at him again. Searching with intent, I looked into his eyes. I had looked at the same eyes in the mirror when I shaved. I knew these eyes; mine. I realized that the monster was a part of me and wanted to escape as well.

We blended into one person and then slowly made our way along the water's edge. I did not know which direction to take, so I paused for a moment, and got in touch with my surroundings. Then I felt a cool breeze of air coming from in front of me. I moved in that direction, ever so slowly, letting my feet take whatever time they needed to be sure of their next step. Eventually I was able to see faint rays of light in front of me. I then found a set of granite steps covered with moss and moisture. I started to climb the stairs, though I felt weak. I looked up, there was no end in sight. I felt my efforts were useless, but I was scared that the monster within might come out and terrify me, so I kept going, one step at a time.

After a while, I noticed the steps were becoming drier and had less moss on them. I could smell a change in the air. It didn't smell quite as musty and old as before. I looked down to see how far I had come, and it looked like a long way, perhaps a hundred yards or so. It was dark and narrow down there. I looked up and thought I saw light. Could it be the top?

I got excited about thinking it was the top, but then all of the sudden I felt uneasy. Where was I going? I knew the cave, it was familiar, but that, way up there, that was a place where I had never been. What was that place? What would I do when I got there? Who would be there?

I stopped. I was scared, frozen in fear about what lay ahead. Just then Vida appeared in my seemingly realistic dream.

"Why have you stopped, Eric?" Vida asked.

"I, uh, I'm scared, I don't know what to do."

"What do you want to do?" He held out his hand.

"I want to not be scared!"

"Why are you scared?"

"I'm not sure. I mean, I don't know what's up there," I aimed my head up toward the top of the stairs. "It could be bad!"

"You have fear," he stated.

"Exactly. I'm afraid to go forward, but I don't want to go back there, either." I pointed to the bottom of the stairs. "What should I do?"

"Be where you are, Eric," he said in a peaceful manner.

"What?" I focused my attention on Vida.

"Be where you are. Are you scared to be where you are?"

"I don't think so." I thought for a moment. How did I feel at the place where I was? I sensed no danger and became less troubled. "I feel okay about where I am."

"Do you want to stay where you are?"

"No, I don't think so. No." I was sure.

"Where do you want to be?" Vida squatted and picked up a stone.

"Somewhere safe."

"Where is that?"

"Up there?" I pointed toward the top.

"Do you know what's up there?" Vida nodded his head in the direction of the opening.

"No! That's why I'm scared!"

"Fear comes from not being where you are, Eric. You want to be somewhere else, and so you project your thoughts to the future and try to predict or anticipate the outcome. In doing so, you fantasize about how things might turn out exactly as you want them to. Then you think about how the outcome may vary from what you desire to what you dread. The fluctuation creates fear and anxiety in you."

"How do I get rid of my fear?"

"Be where you are. Live in the present, for this moment is all we have. Focus on the here and now and devote all your energy to the moment of now. Accept everything that is in the now moment as a gift and be grateful for the gift. This moment, the moment you are in, contains everything you need and is as it should be." Vida stood.

"What do you mean?" I asked.

"All of the forces of the Universe have brought you to this moment. You can only do something about where you are now."

"Now? This moment? But what about when I get up there?"

"You aren't up there, yet. All your energy should be here and now. Reliving the past or projecting the outcome of the future is a waste of the energy you require for the present. The past is over with and you can't go back and change it. Nothing you can do or think can alter one second of the past, nor can you control the outcome of the future because it isn't here yet. Like the donkey chasing the carrot, you have been conditioned to plan and to live for the future. To sacrifice now for future rewards, you have been told, is the way you should live, but by sacrificing the now moment for a future that does not exist, you lose what is here in your present world."

"Like what?" I leaned against the wall.

"We lose the miracle of this one unique moment. The future is the future, and by focusing on that, we lose our power over the present, which is precisely where we need our power; here and now."

"What power?"

"The power of creation, but that's for later. For now, just be where you are." He tossed the stone down the steps.

"I'm here." It made sense to me.

"Know the direction you want to go and take each step as it comes to you. Experience this step for what it is and keep moving forward. Each step is its own moment, in and of itself."

"So, I focus on this step, and don't sweat the next."

"There's no need to project about what lies in front of you, or to dwell on what lies behind. Just move forward and be where you are at that moment."

Vida gestured forward with his hand and smiled, placed his other hand on my shoulder and said, "You are doing the right thing Eric."

With a wink of his eye, he was gone.

In my dream, I sat on the step where I was and focused on the moment and listened to how I felt. I was scared, but I felt better knowing that I would be okay if I kept moving and was clear about my direction. The lesson was basic to the new life I was choosing to live. I knew I was not supposed to stay on that step. That much was clear. I also knew I could not return to the bottom of the cave. I was clear on that, too. So I kept on going, up and up, one step at a time.

When I finally reached the top, the bright sun was overhead. I paused and stood in the mouth of the cave and looked around to get oriented. The forest was thick with trees and vegetation. I was on the top of a giant mountain. I decided to walk to a clearing out beyond the mouth of the cave, staying within a few quick steps of the cave's entrance. After a few minutes of looking around, I turned back toward the opening of the cave. I knew I had to leave it, yet a part of me wanted to stay. I felt sad about leaving, but a clear voice within told me I had to move on.

"Good-bye, you old cave. I'm going to miss you." Tears welled up in the corners of my eyes. "I have to go." Sadness filled my heart and I felt a tug toward the cave as I turned to walk away.

I looked over to the side, and saw Michele and my children. I went over to them. They looked sad, too, as though they didn't understand what I was doing. I wanted to put the children in a safe place, because I knew I had a journey to take, and I had to go alone.

"Go ahead and say good-bye, to them if you want," an unfamiliar female said.

Startled, I turned to find a young woman in a lavender chiffon dress and robe. She had long dark shiny hair, a clear complexion and deep green eyes.

"Who are you?"

"I am Sheila. I have been sent to start you on your pilgrimage."

"Pilgrimage? Where?"

"Please say good-bye first." She motioned to Michele and the children. I turned back to them.

"I've gotta go, but I'll be back for you, I promise." I gave each one a hug and a kiss and whispered, "I love you," in each child's ear. Then I stood in front of Michele. We had been together for many years, but it was time to leave. I tried to find words to describe what I was feeling at that moment. I was sad to leave, but knew I had to go. Deep inside, a voice called me to a solitary sojourn.

"Michele, I, I need to move on."

"Go Eric, just go, damn you." Michele was hurt, deeply hurt. I felt her anger in those six words. My leaving must have destroyed her. She was suffering, and I was in no condition to help. I had to help myself, if I were to stay alive.

"Good-bye, Michele," I said softly with remorse.

No reply. She tightened her lips and choked back her tears.

I turned away and walked toward Sheila. "Okay, let's get going." We walked off and as I turned to see the children, they had moved on.

Sheila spent some time acquainting me with the forest. She was patient and kind. She showed me what plants I could eat, and which ones were harmful.

"You should eat these plants and berries. Please, do not eat the animals. You can substitute these nuts." She showed me how to remove pine nuts and eat them raw. They really weren't bad.

"When the wind blows through the trees and their tops bend to and fro, seek the higher ground, for rains will follow and may flood the path temporarily." She taught me some other things I should know about survival and living in harmony with the planet. Then said, "It's time for you to go now."

"Go where?" I was not ready to leave.

"Follow your Path of Truth, Eric."

"Where does it go?" Perhaps if I asked enough questions, she might have stayed longer. My thinking was mistaken.

"Just follow your Path, Eric, you will know." With that, Sheila vanished.

I looked around and saw two paths. Which one was right? The one on the left was closest, so I went there and stood looking down it for some sign or indication that it was the right way to go. Nothing. I felt no feelings. Other than an empty gut and a cold chest, there were no sensations.

I walked over to the path on the right and looked for an indication that it was the correct one to follow. Nothing. No sign, just a path. "You will know." I kept hearing those words in my mind, "but how could I be sure?" I wondered.

I went back and forth for a while, looking for a sign, something, anything that could be taken for a divine clue, but there was none. I became frustrated. Back and forth I walked again and again. Finally, I gave up and sat down. I noticed gentle energy emanating from the path on the right. I studied it for a few minutes and decided to go in that direction. The closer I got, the stronger the energy became. It felt comfortable.

I walked over to the path on the left. I felt no energy there. I felt anxious and confused about it, so I went back to the one on the right. Again, the energy felt comfortable and peaceful. I felt clear about it, so I decided to give it a try. I cautiously walked down the path.

That's when the dream ended. Actually, it was interrupted, not over.

"Good-morning, Mr. Crane, it's six-thirty." Although the nurses were polite, they had no sympathy when it came time to wake-up. "I need to check your vitals."

They always needed my vitals. Like some religious ritual, my vital signs were taken each morning and several times a day. The hours of recalling the past and the intensity of my dreams had made time go by so fast it seemed as though my vitals were being checked every five minutes.

"Here's your breakfast." She pointed to the tray-table.

Once again, I removed the magic plate cover and found grits, eggs and sausage. The West ate potatoes for breakfast, and the South had grits. I liked grits. I stirred them up into my eggs, and the mixture was delicious. The toast was cold and dry, but, that's hospital food for you.

I got up and took a shower, the first one in a couple of days, and it felt exquisite. I was ready to go home, but the doctor wanted just one more day to observe me.

I got back into the bed, and the phone rang.

"Well, hello, son."

Somehow in all that had been going on I had forgotten to call my mother. I felt embarrassed. "Moma! What a surprise! How are you?"

"I'm just fine. The question is, how are you?"

"Oh, pretty good. I've had a lot of time to rest and think."

"Well, good. What have you been thinking about?"

Did she really want to know? Should I tell her? Why not? After all, she's my mother. If anyone would believe that an angel had appeared to me, surely Moma would!

"You probably won't believe this, but I had a visit from a being that told me he was my Guardian Angel. His name is Abliel."

"Oh, boy! What else did he have to say?"

Maybe she was buying it, and maybe she was just going along with me. Either way, I had opened my mouth and I decided I might as well go for it. "He has told me a lot, mostly about love and opening up and changing things in my life."

"Sounds good. What does he look like?"

"Well, I haven't actually seen him like I see people; I've just kind of experienced his presence for the last few days. It's like I hear his voice, but it's not like physically hearing, it's more intuitive, you know? But its clear. Very clear, and it's distinctive. I know what my voice sounds like, when I think to myself, and Abliel's voice is much different. It's clear, distinct, warm, familiar and friendly, like it's someone I've known for a long, long time."

There was silence on the other end. Finally, I heard her sniffle. She was crying.

"Are you okay?" I asked, hoping I had not said too much.

"Oh, Eric. I had a dream the other night about you, and there was a large person clothed in white light. He told me you were okay and for me not to worry. It seemed so real that when I woke up it took me a few minutes to remember where I was, but I felt better, and I knew you were all right."

"Wow! So you don't think I'm crazy?"

"I didn't say that." She giggled. "No, son. I'm sure you're not crazy, and I'm glad you're okay. I hope this Abliel fellow can help you, that's all."

"Well, I'll keep you posted." I tried to reassure her.

"I better go now." Moma did not talk much long distance.

"Thanks for calling."

"You get some rest, okay?"

"How can I not? See you later."

"Bye-bye," she quietly said.

I hung up the telephone, grabbed my notebook and wrote down the phone conversation. It was amazing that she had that dream. I wondered if Abliel had come to visit her.

Then my eyes began to read over what I had written up to that point. I resumed my writing at the business trip in Birmingham where I had gotten drunk. I went back in my mind to that morning. I remembered feeling it was time to push the rope. That was an expression that described how I felt about work. I felt I was putting in a lot of effort toward an impossible goal. It felt like I was truly trying to push a rope.

On that morning, I got up, took a shower, got dressed and went to the elevators. My head ached and I felt like the room was spinning. I began to sweat and shake. "I need a drink," I told myself. A little hair of the dog would fix things, so I walked across the street to a convenience store and bought a can of beer, drank it and went to breakfast. Things would get better; they had to.

They didn't. I lost a major deal that day. I should have sold it. It would have been the best deal we had put together yet, but I lost it. I rarely lost deals. What was wrong with me? What happened? I didn't want to call the office and tell them, not yet anyway. It was eleven in the morning and I was a loser. I went to a gas station to fill up the car and to get a six-pack. Then I got on I-20 and headed for Atlanta. An hour later, I pulled over to get another six-pack. When I finally got to Atlanta, I found a bar and ordered a scotch. I missed my children. I lost a major deal. I thought I was a born loser. It was two-thirty in the afternoon, and I was drunk. I was lonely, hungry, pissed-off and tired as hell.

The next thing I knew, it was past midnight and the bar I found that afternoon was closing. Miguel, the bartender called me a cab. I couldn't remember where I lived because I had recently moved into an apartment, so the cabby took me to a Holiday Inn. Tomorrow would be another day, but who cared? Sleep, I told myself. Just get some sleep. And I did. As I had done the previous night, I passed out on the bed with my clothes still on.

The phone rang. "Mr. Crane, are you going to check out, sir?"

People in the south are so polite, everyone is a sir or a ma'am. "Yeah, what time is it?"

"It's one-thirty, Mr. Crane."

"Morning?"

"No sir, it's the afternoon. Are you okay, sir?"

"Yeah, sure, uh, gimme a few minutes, will'ya?"

"No problem, sir."

"Thanks." I slammed the phone in its cradle.

I had missed a nine o'clock staff meeting. I had lost a major deal, and missed a meeting. Now what? "Man, Crane, when you screw up you do it right!" I said to myself.

I had to call Frank, but what would I say? There was nothing to say.

I could make up something. Car trouble? Right. I had a new Mark VII. I met someone? Sure! I'm on my own now; he would understand that. But why hadn't I called before? I couldn't think of a good lie.

I decided to call him and suggest we meet for dinner. We had a good enough relationship that I could confide in him and get out of trouble.

"Frank, this is Eric," I said, anticipating the worst.

"Where the hell have you been?" He was upset.

"Uh, hey, let's get together and talk tonight. How about dinner?"

"Are you all right, Eric?" Frank was fishing.

"Yeah, I'll see you at Longhorn's at six." A moment passed.

"Okay, see you there." He hung up his phone first.

Good, I thought. If I could put on enough of a "poor me" story, everything would be okay, although somehow I knew deep inside it wasn't.

Frank was never late for an appointment or a meeting. I guess it was his twenty years of IBM training that made him that way. I was hoping that night would be different, but there he was, pulling into a parking place at five-fifty-seven.

I had been seated in a booth by the window since five and waved to Frank as he crossed the parking lot to the sidewalk. "Now," I began rehearsing my speech in my mind, making sure I had all the angles figured out. I was only half-way through it when Frank walked up to the booth.

"Traffic was unbelievable tonight!" Frank always had an opener.

"Yeah, it's hard to believe this used to be the country." We lived in Roswell, a suburb of Atlanta that had undergone rapid growth in the previous ten years. If there was a half acre of available land, a strip mall was not far behind.

"Can I get you guys anything?" A young waitress had followed Frank to the booth.

"Glenlivet, rocks." My newly automatic reaction to that question.

"Stoley's on the rocks." Frank liked vodka.

"So, had a good trip?" Frank looked at me sarcastically.

"Frank, I apologize."

"Look Eric, I know you're having some hard stuff to go through. I can empathize a little bit, but the problem is you aren't pulling your weight and the other guys are asking questions."

"Hey, this is none of their business!" My anger flared.

"Yes, but it is my business, and I need your help," he sternly said.

"Sure Frank, anything for you." I stopped being defensive.

"I want you to take some time and go get some help." He looked serious.

"For what?"

"You're drinking a lot these days."

"Ah, hey that's nothing. I mean it's being away from the kids, you know what I mean!" There was panic in my gut.

"I mean it. I want you to get help with this."

"Look, give me a few more months. I'm seeing a therapist, and I'll watch it, I promise."

"Here you are guys, Glenlivet for you, sir, and Stoley's for you. Are you ready to order?" The waitress could not have came back too soon.

"Not yet, thanks." I wanted to know what Frank was thinking.

"Okay, I'll be back." She went to the next table.

I proposed a toast. "Here's to friendship and good business!"

He accepted. "To friendship and good business and your health."

We ate dinner and talked about business, wives and children. Afterwards we went home. Frank had agreed to give me a little more time. I had dodged a bullet, but when was the next one coming, and more importantly, from whom?

My writing was interrupted by a familiar voice. "Good morning, Eric."

It was the Reverend Dick Dunlop from the local Methodist church Sonnie and I occasionally attended. "Hey, Dick, how are you?"

"The question is how are you?"

"I feel better, thanks. I've been thinking a lot about my life."

"Anything in particular?"

"I've had a number of messages from the spirit world. One of them says he's my Guardian Angel, and the other claims to be a Spirit Guide."

Dick appeared to be okay with my statement. "People frequently get divine messages from God. They come in many forms. It's not so important what the form is, as long as you hear the message clearly and are able to learn from it. The most important thing is that you don't fight the power of these messengers. The Bible is full of stories about people who have received messages from angels and Spirit Guides. Some of them fought the experience, such as Jacob. Others gave up their resistance and let the message transform their lives, like the apostle Paul."

I flashed back to my Bible training. "Yeah, I suppose so."

"Listen with your heart, Eric, and if it is truly from God, and I believe from what you have told me that these messengers are from God, you will know it beyond any shadow of a doubt, for God's people know his voice."

"Thanks."

"Do you mind if I offer a prayer?"

"Not at all; in fact, I'd like it."

He closed his blue eyes, bowed his half-bald head and prayed. "Thank you, Father, for the messengers sent to Eric who have carried to him the message of your Love. Thank you for the healing he has received here in the hospital and for the rest he so needed."

He put his hand on my hand. "Now, Eric, I bless you in the name of the Father that you will continue to learn Wisdom and Love. That you will gladly follow God's will for your life and that you will allow God to work in you and through you that others may come to know His divine Love as expressed in His only begotten Son, Jesus the Christ. In his name I bless you, Amen."

There was a moment of silence.

"Thank you," I whispered softly.

"Get some rest." He winked at me, squeezed my arm and left.

I laid there quietly. The feeling of love was so powerful that I was completely still, lying in awe in it's presence.

"What he says is correct."

"Hey, Vida."

"When you stop fighting, you will receive." He walked in.

"What?" I asked.

"Life. When you stop fighting life, you will receive life, only more abundantly." He sat in the chair across from my bed.

"How so?"

"Life can be lived at any level you choose. You can choose a life of abundance, a life of scarcity, a life of riotous living, a life based on fear or a life based on Love. A way has been set before you so that you can choose. A better way. A more excellent way. Only you can choose your way.

"You are being given this opportunity to learn about Love so that you will desire to choose it and, by so choosing, have Abundant Life."

"You mean rich?" Suddenly I was more interested.

"Spiritually rich. When Jesus asked the rich young lawyer to sell all he had and follow him, the lawyer was unable to do so, because he was rich. That doesn't necessarily mean wealthy with money. Rich in this sense means rich with Ego. The lawyer was so rich in Ego that he was unable to follow the Christ Light within his own being. The challenge to sell all he had was a challenge to get rid of his ego and follow a spiritual path."

In all my years of reading that scripture, I had never considered that interpretation.

"God is everything, is in everything and has everything. Don't think the riches of the world are yours. The riches of the world belong to God, as does the Universe. What you have is an illusion of wealth. There is only Love. If you have Love, you are truly wealthy. The riches of the world do not create Love, it only creates an illusion."

"But what's that got to do with an Abundant Life?"

"Abundant Life may include monetary wealth for some, but at its deeper level, it is an abundance of Love, a spiritual richness that can only come from God's unconditional Love. There is no other way but through Love. This Love is given through grace. It is a gift. It is free. God's Grace gives us Abundant Life through the power of pure Love."

A chord in my heart had been struck. I had a constant struggle between having a lot of money in the bank and being worthy to serve God at the same time. I'd heard wealthy people couldn't enter the kingdom of God, but now it made more sense. I had been wrong in my beliefs in two senses. I had focused on worldly riches, and I had never considered that my Ego was my problem. I had struggled my entire adult life to acquire money, but had felt it never came to me in abundance. All the while I was attending church thinking I had Love, but I had only an illusion of Love, not its essence.

My mind wandered back to the conversation in the restaurant with Frank. I felt as though I had dodged a bullet. But what was really happening to me?

– *Nine* –

AFTER THE MEETING IN THE RESTAURANT WITH FRANK, I DECIDED TO
get back into the swing of things at work by going the extra mile, making sure I was the first one there in the morning, and the last to leave
at night. I wanted everyone to know I was pulling my weight.

A year had passed since I left Spokane, and I was still not clear on
what was going on with me, except that I could not see any way to work
things out with Michele. She had no desire to move to Atlanta. In fact,
she had moved to her hometown and was dating a guy seriously.

I, too, was seeing other women, but nothing ever got beyond a couple of dates. I went to movies, concerts, exhibitions, boat rides, played
softball and partied with some of the nicest women on the planet, but
nothing ever clicked with any of them. I was having fun, but felt nothing like I had felt for Donna. I wondered if I would ever feel that again.

One Sunday morning in January, I decided to stay in. The weather
was cold, by Atlanta's standards, and overcast. I figured I would stay
home and read.

I had been reading books about divorce, male issues, psychology,
love and spirituality. I was reading a book about multiple selves and
was getting confused. How could you be what you aren't?

That thought stayed with me as I looked out the window in my
hospital room. Puffy white clouds hung in the blue Georgia sky.
The concept of multiple selves remained somewhat of a mystery,
and my mind got lost in the sky. That's when I heard Vida's voice.

"Confusing, huh?"

"Vida, where did you? … Oh yeah, I forgot." Vida came and went as he pleased. "Yes, it's confusing. How can you be something you're not?"

"It's really quite simple," he said authoritatively.

Everything was really quite simple to Vida.

"We are creations. You have to remember that, first and foremost, and you must never forget it. We are creations. There is a Power in the universe that is creative and divine. This Power created all you see on this planet and all that you see in the sky."

"Yeah, sure, like on the first day, God created the heavens and the earth and all that stuff." Sarcasm is easy for me.

"That's what you believe from your traditions. The truth is greater than that, but that's for another time. For now, know that you were created by a powerful, divine and holy Creator and the essence of that Creator is in you."

"What?" I struggled with the last part.

"Maybe this will help. Remember your story about creation?"

I nodded.

"It also says that God breathed into man the Breath of Life. You know what that is?"

"No," I replied with naivete.

"Nephesh."

"Nephesh?" I repeated it in a question like manner.

"Nephesh. It means the life force or that part of the Creator that is in all of us. We all share a divineness with our Creator. We all have the same life force."

"Then how did we get to where we fight and kill and have wars and divorce and steal and all that stuff?" I asked contentiously.

"When you were born, you were pure. As you grew, you began to learn that there are limits. The first word you learned was 'no' and the first commands from your parents were commands that told you what not to do."

He had a point.

"You learned incorrectly from your parents, who learned the same incorrect lessons from their parents, who learned them from their parents, and so on and so on. Generations of incorrect teachings and ineffective patterns of how to deal with life have influenced the person you have turned out to be." Vida's tone was nonjudgemental.

"Does that mean the Bible stories are wrong?"

"It's not about being right, or wrong. If you had been born in Japan you might have learned different values than those you learned here. The point is you learned about life through the eyes of your parents, who themselves were raised in the American Judeo-Christian society.

"As you grew, you went outside of the home and learned more dysfunctional beliefs from your friends and their parents. You learned incorrect ways of seeing the world at school, at church and in your neighborhood. All that you learned from these sources was to eventually become part of you. If there was a flaw in the model, you absorbed it, and made it part of you." Vida stood and moved to the window.

"Like, when I was five years old, and Richard Henry told me about the boogie-man. That scared the crap out of me. But as I got older, I learned there was no boogie-man."

"Good. You get the point." He was looking out the window, then turned to me. "When you came into adolescence, you began to learn even more about yourself and the world around you. All through your teenage years, you had more experiences that added to your growth. And grow you did, Eric. You learned a lot then."

He was right. I did learn a lot during high school. Vietnam war protests were going on and drugs had become the thing to do. My generation had come alive during the "Age of Aquarius". We were extremely idealistic in our thinking. The "Establishment" had destroyed the country, and there had to be a revolution in order to change it all. Mandatory retirement for everyone over thirty. Eventually, we all grew up and became part of the "Establishment" we fought against.

"Then Eric, you became an adult. You got married and left your life dream behind and joined the business world. You 'settled' for less than you were created to be. You closed yourself off to others and to your Self, thus denying the Nephesh in you. In other words, you sinned."

"Ah, come on, Vida, are you going to start preaching to me after all this?" I had heard preaching all my life and now regarded preachers with skepticism.

"You don't understand." He shook his head.

"I understand that all my life I've heard that religion stuff, and I'm miserable. I'm not gonna listen to it anymore, so if that's all you have to say, then say good-bye." My mood suddenly changed.

Vida moved to the bed. "Sin isn't something that you do, like you have been taught to believe. That's the problem. Religion has taught you that sin is breaking God's commandments, when, in actuality, they are primarily man-made rules. That's not sin."

"Huh?" That statement was contrary to what I was taught.

"The original word means to miss the mark. Sin is a term used in archery, when someone misses the bullseye, the mark, or center. You have sinned because you have missed your Center."

"My center?" My interest was piqued.

"Yes, your Center, that part of you that is divine, that is Nephesh. It's your True Center, the essence of the Creator and all life in the universe, and you've missed it. You have been living in a False Center, like so many others do."

"False Center?" I sat up and crossed my legs, listening attentively.

"It's a false self. You think it's real, but it's manmade, and therefore false. It's full of false beliefs, thoughts and patterns. A False Center is one wherein you believe you are who you truly are and who others see you, but it's not who you were created to be."

"It's not?"

Vida sat in the chair. "Look, when Jesus conversed with the woman at the well, he talked about rivers of living water that flowed from the belly. The living water comes from the True Center. False Centers require you to fuel them externally with things from the outside, like work, alcohol and religion."

I considered my drinking and my working hours. I drank heavily, and worked nonstop. There was never enough booze, or time. I wanted more.

Vida spoke more. "The True Center is filled by the Creator. It's internal, fueled by divine Love, the only real power in the Universe. The True Center cannot be filled by external sources. Nothing you do can alter that. You and every creation in the Universe have been made with a True Center that knows only pure Love as its source."

"So how do I find out about this 'True Center'?"

"You don't need to 'find out' about it. You've been trying to 'find out' all your life. You think you can just 'figure it out' and then build your system around it. But this is different. You can't 'figure it out.' You can't 'find out' about it. It is what it is, and it's been inside you since birth. You need to learn how to allow the Creator's life force to flow within you and to enlarge your True Center."

"How do I do that?"

"You must change, starting with those things in your False Center that are keeping you from the True Center."

"Like what?"

"Addictions, for starters." He crossed his legs.

Here we go again, the "booze" sermon, I thought.

"It's not just booze Eric."

"That's not fair. If I can't read your thoughts, then you shouldn't be able to read mine!" I shook my finger at him.

"You have opened yourself to me, Eric. Its not that I read your thoughts, I am aware of what's in your heart, because I am attuned to your energy." His voice was tranquil.

"So what else, besides booze?" I backed down.

"An addiction is anything one uses to alter one's mood. It could be food, cigarettes, alcohol, drugs, work, church, sex and so on."

"But those things aren't wrong."

"It's not about wrong Eric. It's about things that keep you from your True Center. Things that take you to a place where you are not in the present, where you don't have to feel your feelings, where you can avoid what's happening at that moment within you."

Had I used alcohol or work to avoid something, I wondered?

"When you use drugs and alcohol to numb feelings, you are living in your false, ego driven center. Work, church, food and sex are not of themselves harmful to you, or to anyone, for that matter. They can become addictions that rob you of your personal power. Real power, or the life force, Nephesh, comes from the Eternal Source. The Source is in your True Center, the God-essence within." He pointed to his heart.

"You may recall the Master taught the kingdom of God is within. When you are living through Ego, you are not receiving power from your True Center, but rather, you have an illusion of power from an external source, such as an addiction. By its nature this illusory power is fleeting, requiring more. It's like the gas tank of a car. It needs constant refilling from an external source." Vida stood as he spoke.

"The True Center is eternal. Its source is the One Source of the Universe, which is omnipotent and infinite and has no beginning or no end. Only through living in your True Center can you experience Soul growth.

"So you see, Eric," he said as he moved closer, "you sin by missing the mark of your True Center. That which would take you out of your True Center is what is sinful. It's not a list of do's and don'ts, it's what you are, what you think and how you feel."

"So what you're saying is, I'm living in a False Center?" I asked.

"We can start there, Eric. But it's more than that. Others have not caused your misery. You have created your life and how you feel inside is the result of your choices. Your years of religious training and service originated from good intention. Unfortunately you believed church was the answer. When that failed to bring joy you turned to alcohol." He sat on the corner of my bed.

"The problem is your religion teaches a step ladder approach to the Divine. Spirituality is nothing like a stepladder. It is more like a spring fed lake. It comes from the connection of the True Center to our Creator. It comes from within and flows outward into the Universe, where it connects with all other life, so that the Circle of Life is complete. It has no beginning and has no end." He waved his hands about.

I had to think about that one for a moment. The concept was new.

"Think about the water on planet Earth. The water evaporates into the atmosphere and becomes a cloud that rains back onto the earth and eventually flows to the seas. There is never any 'new' water. The total amount of water is always the same. The cycle has no beginning and knows no end, a circle of life. It is natural and is of the Creator."

It began to make sense. I thought about how I had used church to keep me from my True Center. I wondered what else had kept me from finding it. "So what else is in my way?"

"What do you think?" Vida looked serious.

"What do you mean?" I knew the answer, but I was coy.

"What else is in your False Center that prevents you from being in your True Center?" Vida leaned forward.

Of course he was talking about the booze. I was drunk every night and on weekends too.

"The alcohol?" I asked, hoping for a negative response.

"Alcohol, like church is not bad. It's when it is used to numb pain or to escape from life that it interferes with your Soul growth."

"So you think I should cut back?"

"You determine what you should do." He patted my shins.

"Okay, I'll be careful."

Vida looked at me sympathetically. "Please, Eric, for your own good."

"Okay, I'll cut back!"

"Mr. Crane?" The doctor stared at me from the door. I wondered if he thought I was talking to myself.

Vida exited the room.

"I'm afraid I have some bad news for you," he said as he approached my bed.

"What?" I had to shift my mind from Vida to the doctor.

"We've been running some tests, and your liver is abnormally large. Your tri-glycerides are over one thousand when they should be in the one-fifty range. How much do you drink, Mr. Crane?" He looked up.

"What do you mean?"

"How much alcohol do you drink?"

"Oh, well, uh, not that much, I mean I have a beer or two at night and a scotch now and again, but really, it's not out of control, if that's what you mean."

"I haven't said it's out of control. I merely asked how much you were drinking."

"Okay. Well, it's not that much."

"I'm afraid we're going to have to admit you to a treatment center, Mr. Crane. I've spoken to your wife and she agrees that you need help."

"Now wait a minute, Doc! What about what I have to say. I don't have a drinking ...." I was incensed that they did not consult me.

He interrupted me. "Mr. Crane, as your physician, I am ordering you to a treatment facility. Professionally, it is my obligation, and legally, I have the right. You can of course resist it, but I recommend against fighting it. This is for your own good."

I went limp. "So it's just like that?"

"I'm sorry, Mr. Crane, but it's serious."

"So, where do you have in mind?" I said sarcastically.

"Peachtree Recovery Institute. I know a psychiatrist who has privileges there."

"Psychiatrist?" My experience with Dr. Bronson flashed into my mind. "No way."

"It's a requirement, Mr. Crane. You need someone skilled in addiction who can also monitor your physical symptoms."

"And when do I go?"

"I've written the orders. You'll be transferred tomorrow. Meanwhile, I've ordered Antabuse."

"Antabuse?"

"It's what we give people who suffer from alcoholism. If you drink while you take Antabuse, you'll become ill."

"Alcoholism? You think I am an alcoholic?" I challenged him.

"Mr. Crane, I know this is a shock to you, but your liver is starting to go. Your blood indicates it, your triglyceride level is off the chart and you're having tremors. This doesn't happen to people who aren't alcoholic. Its a disease, Mr. Crane, and if you let us treat it, we can help you."

"Great." There was no use in arguing. "Fine, I'll go." I reluctantly agreed.

"Good. I'll call Dr. Smithson at the Institute."

Alcoholic. Great, just great. Now what? Now what's going to happen? "Abliel?"

"Yes, Eric?"

"What the hell's going on? I thought I was learning about Love and my Path and the True Center and stuff like that."

"You are. Just let this happen. It is all a part of the Divine Order of the Universe. Be patient, be open and be honest. You will see that this is for your highest good."

Tears formed in my eyes.

"The True Center Vida taught you is real. You have been living in a False Center for some time, and now you must find your True Center. The time has come for you to stop running. Think only of your Truth now. The next decision you make will bring you one step closer to your Truth. That is all for now."

The remainder of the day was spent thinking about my True Center. How had I created a False Center? What did I have to do to get rid of it and to be in my True Center? I fell asleep thinking about it.

I had a strange dream that night. I was in a large room of people, some I knew and others I did not know. I felt uncomfortable, as though I didn't fit, and when I looked at myself, I was in my underwear. I wanted to hide, to run away from the crowd. I felt as though everyone was looking at me and laughing, but strangely, no one was actually looking at me. They were simply going about their business.

I felt deep shame and embarrassment. I tried to cover up the fact that I was in my underwear by trying to blend into the group, but I felt tremendously awkward. I was there, but I was not a part of anything. I felt alone.

The scene changed. I was in high school. Again, I was wearing my underwear, and again I felt embarrassed and shamed. I wanted to run and hide.

Then I saw a gorgeous woman. She had long golden hair, like smooth silky ribbons. Her skin was completely unblemished and her body was firm and shapely. She was dressed in a tight knit black dress that hugged every curve on her body. The nipples of her plump firm breasts were outlined in the fabric of her short dress that stopped just below her pear-shaped buttocks, exposing her exquisite thighs. I looked down to her knees, where her calves curved perfectly into her ankles and heels. She had on black silk stockings and wore black leather stiletto heels.

Her eyes were a mixture of gray and blue and her eyebrows were full. Her nose was slight, and her lips glistened. Her face was clear and smooth with high cheek bones and a round chin.

As our eyes met I felt a nervous jump in my heart and a warm swelling in my groin. I wanted to taste her.

She began to undress, and the powerful, growing expectation of an erotic encounter filled me with a sense of euphoria. The blood flowed to my penis and I got an instant erection as her clothes fell to the floor.

Finally, she stood before me, completely nude. I went to her and kissed and licked her neck and shoulders. I felt my nakedness on hers. My stomach touched hers, and our thighs and legs wrapped around each other like pretzels.

I penetrated, when instantly the beautiful creature turned into an old hag. Her unkempt and stringy long gray hair fell sporadically over her bony shoulders. Her wrinkled ashen face had a large mole with a single black hair growing from it. She had no teeth and her eyes were dull and lifeless.

I felt a deep sense of horror and panic. I quickly tried to get off her but she pulled me ever closer. I fought, using all my strength, but it was fruitless. She had a powerful vise-grip on me and would not release her clutch. I panicked. I was terrified at the thought of being in the wretch's powerful grip. I was doomed to a slow, suffocating death.

I woke up abruptly to bright, obnoxious fluorescent lights over the bed. I was never so happy to see the swing shift nurse, who was making her last round before clocking out. It was six-thirty.

"Man!" I thought, "what the hell was that? ... Thank you nurse!"

I laid in the warmth and security of the bed and looked out into the darkness of the morning. The dream had seemed real. My heart was beating rapidly as the sense of terror carried over from the dream to my awake state. It took me a few minutes to get a sense of bearing. What was the meaning of the dream? I pondered the thought over and over in my mind.

"Good morning, Eric." Vida's familiar voice felt comforting.

"Vida, it's early!" I said with a happy-to-see-you tone.

"Rest well?"

"Yes, well actually I want to ask you about a nightmare I just had." I recounted my dream in as much detail as possible. It annoyed me that so often after a really good dream, I could wake up and forget it in no time, but give me a nightmare and it remained clear for weeks. "Why have good dreams, if you can only remember the nightmares?" I thought.

I finished telling him about it. "So what does it mean?"

"Hmm. Remember our discussion of the target and sin and the True and False Centers." He sat on the corner of my bed.

"Yes," I replied.

"Your dream about being in your underwear in a room of people and your subsequent feeling of embarrassment is part of the True and False Center.

"We are all spirit. Before you were created as a human, with a physical body, you existed as spirit. You brought that spirit here to the planet and put it into your human body where it shares a body with a brain that can reason and think on its own." He paused and looked at me to see if I comprehended.

"Okay." My response was a hybrid statement and question.

He resumed. "Your brain is a reasoning factory in your head where you develop your Ego. So you are a spiritual being in a physical body that has an Ego. There is another aspect of you called the emotional body. This is where your feelings like anger, happiness, joy, rage, contentment, etc. are stored."

Vida made things simple for me. I appreciated that.

"Another way to look at it is to call your True Center your Spiritual Center and your False Center your Ego Center. The Ego makes you feel separate and apart from everything else in your world. Your Ego says you are separate, you do not fit in and you are not connected to your universe or to those around you. This in turn causes you to feel the feelings you now feel; a feeling of being in the group, but not part of the group, of being there, but not really being there. In turn you feel no peace, no serenity, no rest. You feel like there's a hole in you, like something's missing, like you are an outcast."

I thought about how often I felt like I did not fit into the group. Alcohol changed that. With booze, I felt like I fit into any group.

Vida went on, saying, "Being in your underwear is not being clothed properly. You didn't get dressed like everyone else. You did not grow and develop in a healthy environment. Your dysfunctional past has made you less mature than you otherwise might have been, had you had an opportunity to experience normal, healthy development."

I remember reading something like that when I first moved to Atlanta. Character disorders came from missing certain developmental stages in childhood.

"You are embarrassed because you are not part of the group. You don't fit in. You want desperately to fit in, but you don't. You are not one of them, although you are in the same room and the same high school. You would do anything to be one of the group, to feel connected. Because you don't fit in, you want to flee, either physically or emotionally." He shifted and crossed his leg.

What Vida was saying seemed right. I frequently felt that way, as if I weren't a part of anything. When I went to a party, I felt separate from everyone else, but the moment I had a scotch, Prest-O, Change-O!, I suddenly fit in. I was connected as long as I drank. The problem was that there was never enough to drink to keep me connected. I just passed out. The next day, I felt separate and apart from everyone again.

He kept on speaking, "The school is a place of learning, and because it is a high school, you are progressing in your lessons and are at the next level of learning, even though you still want to flee because you feel out of place, humiliated."

Progressing? I was going to an alcohol treatment center. That was progress? "Surely he's joking," I thought.

"When you met the beautiful woman, the attraction overpowered you. You ran to her. You romanticized and fantasized about what you would do with her. When you embraced her the illusion of feeling connected felt real to you."

I thought beautiful women could transform me. Sonnie was pretty. The attraction was electric. Indeed, I was intoxicated by her allure, and thought I could be complete if I had her.

"The woman changed before your eyes, and as she turned into someone ugly, you became terrified, as if death itself had you in its grip." Vida stood and moved to the window.

"Terrified" was putting it lightly, I thought.

"The woman represents alcohol Eric. You see it as an escape, as a connection to the world around you. You romanticize it and have fantasies about what it will do for you. Eventually, as you partake, its face changes and makes matters worse. It doesn't have to be alcohol, it could be anything that keeps you from your True Center."

I felt uncomfortable. He hit another home run.

"This, Eric, is how your False Center works. It is Ego-based. Your finite Ego is separate from infinite spirit. Ego is manmade. It grows from the process of socialization. It offers no hope. It is where you feel shame and humiliation. When you are in Ego, you feel separate and disconnected from others. Each person's Ego is uniquely different from each other's. In the False Center, your Ego demands constant validation. Its insatiable appetite for self-gratification knows no bounds, desiring all the pleasure the world can offer. Greed, power, control, status; the Ego wants it all and it drives you harder and faster to get it."

I had felt shame in my life, but don't we all? Was I different from anyone else? Sure, I wanted the good things in life, but I never considered myself greedy, or a control freak.

"Take what feels right, and leave the rest. Truth is often accepted in small increments." Vida moved away from the window. "Now, as I was saying, spirit exists in Universal Truth. Divine Spirit, from the Creator, fills the universe. Being a spirit, you are naturally one with the Universe. You are connected to all around you.

"Love is the life force of all creation. Your True Center is filled with pure Love. It is divine. The Creator's life force is in all living creatures and creations. The fruit of pure Love is peace. When you experience this Love you feel content, as pure Love places no demands upon you. It quietly calls you to a higher and better way of life."

"My drinking makes me feel connected. But you say that I am a part of all that is. How can that be?" I was confused.

"When you live in your False Center an illusion of being connected comes from external sources. That's why you feel different when you are in your addiction. But there comes a time when the addiction does not work any more because the external source is finite. That's when the lie becomes obvious. The beautiful woman turns into an old hag. The shattered illusion leaves you feeling hopeless, full of guilt, remorse and despair. After all, what else is there, if you do not know your True Center of spirituality?"

"So how do we get to my True Center?" I asked desperately.

"You are like the rich man Jesus referred to in his parable, Eric. You, like the rich man, are rich in Ego. You depend upon your own thinking to get you through life. It is hard for a man rich in Ego to find his True Center. Jesus compared it to a camel entering a city through a needle." He walked to the chair and sat.

"The needle is a passage way through city walls of ancient times. To get through, a camel was unloaded from all its baggage and made to kneel on all fours. This feat is easier for a camel to perform than entering the Kingdom of Heaven is for a man rich in Ego."

"That's not how they interpreted it in the Baptist church," I said smiling.

Vida chuckled. "No, I don't suppose they interpret it that way in many churches. "Your richness of Ego must be unloaded. You must completely empty your Ego, your false self, so you can be filled with Truth and Light. You must be completely honest with yourself and become completely willing to change. You must experience spiritual birth by dying to your False Center and being born to your True Center."

"But how? How do I do it?" I sat up.

"The first step is to be completely honest with yourself. You think you can control your life and the people around you. The truth is, you have no control over others and the harder you try to exercise control, the more things don't work for you. You must see that because of living in a False Center you have created a life of turmoil, devoid of peace.

"Think about all the ways your life has become unmanageable. Above all, be brutally honest, and desire personal change more than anything else in your life. I will leave you now to ponder this."

He left and I laid back in bed and thought about his lesson.

Be honest? I thought I was honest! Was I really that out of touch? Were my addictions controlling me? Had I truly missed the mark?

I got up, went into the bathroom and looked at myself in the mirror. I stared. Stared and then wept.

"Mr. Crane?" It was the nurse.

"In here!" I replied.

"It's time to get you ready for your transfer."

"I'll be out in a minute." I wiped my eyes with a towel. I felt scared, lonely and sad.

"Are you okay?" she asked.

"Fine, fine, I'll be out in just a minute." I stayed for a few seconds, looking at the eyes in the face looking back at me. I thought, "Okay Crane. It's your time. Let's go." I smiled at my reflection, winked and walked out.

"Okay, I'm ready." I got into the wheelchair and she took me to a waiting taxi. What was the next stop?

– Ten –

I NEVER DID ANYTHING IN LIFE HALFWAY, OR AT LEAST I NEVER THOUGHT I did. Every job I did, every relationship I had, every cause I ever fought for, was done at full bore. I had to do it better, quicker or with more energy than anyone else. Not only that, but once I figured something out, I then worked the angles, so that it was a big success, making me the hero.

I walked in the door at the Peachtree Institute. I was confident that if I put all my effort into it I could complete treatment in a couple of days and return to work. An admitting clerk came to greet me.

"Good morning, Mr. Crane." She was in her mid forties, slightly overweight. She wore a light yellow sweater and a white cotton skirt. On her chest was a name tag, Sue Wzcyiewski.

"Morning." I was not in a conversational mood.

"If you'll just follow me," Sue led me down a corridor, through a set of electronically controlled doors that shut and locked behind us. I felt like a prisoner. We went down the corridor and into what she referred to as the processing center.

"Someone will be with you shortly. Please, have a seat. Can I get you anything, coffee, water?"

"Coffee sounds great. Black, thanks."

She disappeared, and I stood in the empty office, waiting for the next person to show up. There was a knock at the door.

"Here's your coffee, Mr. Crane," she handed me a steaming, full styrofoam cup.

"Thanks, Sue." I sipped it in quiet contemplation. I looked at the factory-made prints on the wall and read a poster that said:

"If we are painstaking about this phase of our development, we will be amazed before we are halfway through. We are going to know a new freedom and a new happiness. We will not regret the past nor wish to shut the door on it. We will comprehend the word serenity and we will know peace. No matter how far down the scale we have gone, we will see how our experience can benefit others. That feeling of uselessness and self-pity will disappear. We will lose interest in selfish things and gain interest in our fellows. Self seeking will slip away. Our whole attitude and outlook upon life will change. Fear of people and economic insecurity will leave us. We will intuitively know how to handle situations that used to baffle us. We will suddenly realize that God is doing for us what we could not do for ourselves.

Are these extravagant promises? We think not. They are being fulfilled among us — sometimes quickly, sometimes slowly. They will always materialize if we work for them."

"That's what I want," I said to myself. "A new freedom and a new happiness. Serenity and peace. That's what I've been searching for all my life!" My thoughts were interrupted by a deep southern voice from behind me.

"Mr. Crane?"

"Yes?" I turned to see who it was.

"I'm Dr. Smithson. How are you?" Dr. Smithson was about six feet tall, had a slight build and short blonde hair, parted on the left and combed to the right. He wore a freshly starched white shirt, a semi-conservative blue floral tie and a deep navy blue wool-blend suit. He had on plain black lace-up oxfords.

"Fine. I mean, well you know, I'm here, right?" What else could I say?

"Do you like 'The Promises?'" He gestured to the poster as he moved to sit in the chair behind the small interviewing desk.

"Oh that?" I nodded my head toward the poster I had just read.

"Those are called 'The Promises.' It's part of A.A. Nice, huh?"

"Yeah," I replied nervously, hoping this experience with a psychiatrist would be different than my experience with Dr. Bronson.

He sat in the chair and scooted himself closer to the desk. "So, tell me about yourself, Mr. Crane."

"From when?" I took the seat directly across from him.

"The beginning," he replied unemotionally.

I told him the story. The same story I had told Amy Carlson, except that I brought it up to the present.

"And how about the drinking? How much do you drink?"

"About two or three six packs of beer and a couple bottles of wine and a quart of scotch a week."

"Do you feel like your life is out of control?"

"Yeah, sort of. Really, a lot." There, I said it. I sniffled. Being there made me emotional. Here I was, a successful business executive, yet there I was in the booby hatch. I felt like a total failure.

"Mr. Crane, how often do you cry like this?"

"Oh, about every week or so." I choked back the tears. I thought I had better get it under control, before he thought I was really nuts. "That's stupid, Crane," I thought, "you're in the booby hatch for Christ's sake, can't you admit that you're done in?"

"How long does the crying last?"

"Not long. Maybe a few minutes." I looked at the floor.

"And what do you do to stop it?" He made notes in the file.

"I have a drink." Not true. I had a lot of drinks.

"How about your sleep at night? Do you sleep well, or do you wake up often?"

I paused to think for a moment. "I generally toss and turn, and I wake up a couple of times in the night."

"Are you having fun in your life?" He looked up.

"Ha! Are you kidding? Life's not fun. It's a full-time job." I crossed my legs and shook my foot, a nervous habit I have.

"How's your energy level? Do you wake up ready to go, or do you find it difficult to get out of the bed sometimes?" He resumed taking notes.

"It's hard to get up almost all the time. Some mornings I don't. I just lay there and go back to sleep."

"How long have you felt this way?" He looked directly at me.

"All my life, I suppose," I said in a drab tome.

"Mr. Crane, I want to do some tests. You may be suffering from a form of clinical depression. The good news is that depression is treatable and, with medication, you can get to a normal level of functioning. The bad news is that you have a problem with alcohol, and moreover, if you do suffer from depression, the alcohol is making matters worse, because it's a depressant.

"I'm going to admit you to the Dual Diagnosis Unit. That's where patients are treated for chemical addiction as well as a secondary disease, such as depression. Do you have any questions?" He looked me squarely in the eyes.

"Yeah. How long will I be here?"

"It's difficult to say. A few weeks or more. We will watch it and see how you respond to treatment."

"And what is treatment?" I looked at him with defiance.

"We will start you on anti-depressant medication and monitor the results. In addition, you will attend group sessions and go to A.A. meetings here in the hospital. The purpose is to help educate you about the disease of alcoholism and depression and give you some tools with which to lead a normal and productive life. You will feel much better in a few weeks. Okay?"

"Fine." What else could I say? My idea of getting through treatment in a couple of days was shattered, so I caved in.

"Good. I'll see you tomorrow." He stood and offered me his hand.

"Thanks doc." I stood and we shook hands.

He left and a lady came in and asked me to sign some paperwork. I was then escorted down a long corridor and through another set of electronically locked doors. I was taken to the nurses station and introduced to one of the nurses.

"Hi, my name is Andy." He stuck out his hand to shake mine. People in the South like to shake hands, so we did.

"I'm Eric."

"Good to meet you, Eric. Let me show you to your room." He took me down another corridor to room 202. "This will be your room. You don't have a roommate now, so take either bed."

I put my belongings in a closet and walked over to the window to open the draperies. I decided on the bed closest to the window. I sat on it to give it a try. Not too bad. Then I stretched out and relaxed. "Okay, Crane, you're here; now what?" I mumbled.

"What's that?" Andy thought I was speaking to him.

CONFESSIONS OF A CLOSED MALE

"Nothing, uh, I was just talking to myself." I felt embarrassed.

"We have a lot of that around here." He chuckled. "I'll have someone come to show you around. Put your things away and make yourself comfortable." With that he walked out the door.

A monologue broke out in my head. "Here I am, in the nut house, the funny farm, you know, the place I used to joke about as a kid. The place where only the sick and helplessly insane went. Am I sick and helplessly insane? I must be, or I wouldn't be here. I just can't keep it under control anymore. I want it to stop, to go away and never return, that awful feeling, the Despair, the Darkness, the Oppression of my Soul. The helpless/hopeless feeling deep down in the core of my being. The feeling that life is too much to handle, that there's no way out, no solution, no fun. Just - no, like it's over.

"So now what? I'm here, like countless others before me, and those to follow. Who slept in this steel bed last night? Where is that person today? Did he make it?

"Am I a quitter, a non-hacker? Weak, feeble? Does it matter? I'm here. This is where I am. It's my life, my path. Where do I go from here?"

A voice over the intercom broke my soliloquy.

"Meds, time for meds. All patients requiring meds please come to the nurses' station."

Meds. They go to meds like ducks go to stale bread and crackers. They flock to meds, those pretty capsules of chemicals that make them feel better, sleep better, think better, clearer, breathe easier...the easier, softer way.

There would be no meds for me that morning — my savior would come later.

Thoughts flew through my head at a rapid rate. Then I started to feel sleepy, so I turned over to my side, faced the wall and took a nap.

"Mr. Crane?" It was the doctor, the shrink, the guy with all the answers. I had all the questions, but wanted all the answers. "Can we talk?" He stood in the doorway.

"Sure, I was just resting for a few minutes." I got up and walked to the door. Dr. Smithson moved into the corridor, waiting for me. I followed him down the corridor to an interview room, one of those small six-by-eight foot rooms where patients were taken to for confidential conversations.

"Tell me what's going on now."

Was he kidding? I was feeling crazy and wondering what the hell I was doing in the nut house, and he wanted to know what was going on? I decided I had nothing to lose except to be honest and say what was really going on deep inside. "I feel like I am at the end of the street, that there are no more bends in the road and I'm fresh out of options."

"Please, go on," he said, encouraging me.

"There's a deep, dark feeling of gloom and oppression inside and all around me. There's a monkey on my back to perform this or that for the waiting crowd. I feel no joy, at least not lasting. I've always felt this way. I've always felt like I was under the gun, or under the thumb, like I was a misfit and was always being watched to see if I dared screw up. I'm perpetually looking for some 'thing' that I never seem to be able to find. I know it exists on some level. It doesn't have a name, it's just some 'thing' I am desperately searching for and can never quite seem to find."

Dr. Smithson nodded as he took notes. "How long have you felt like this?"

"Since I was a child. I carried it into my teenage years, when I started drinking and smoking pot. I was a lost soul, drifting with whatever wind seemed to blow by."

"And later?"

"As an adult, I've been miserable trying to earn a living, keeping my nose to the grindstone. The harder I work and fight, the harder things become. It's always work, work, work. There's never time for play. Play is something I used to do as a child. I don't go there anymore. I have no time for play. Life is serious. I have no time, except for the serious stuff. Just push a little harder, make one more sales call, one more deal, and it'll be enough. But there's never 'enough.'"

The doctor made more notes. "Please, continue."

"Well, look at me now. I have no more answers, no hope, and a miserable life."

He lifted his pen from the paper, and looked at me. "Mr. Crane, I'm going to order some tests and medication. I want you to rest here and take time to get to know these people. You'll be here for a few weeks, and at that time we will make a decision on where to go from here. Okay?" He wrote a little more in my file, twisted his pen and placed it in his shirt pocket. Then he stood, ready to leave.

As though I had an option. I could stay there, or go back. If I left, only one thing waited for me, and that was the ultimate solution to all my problems. "Sure, what have I got to lose at this point?" I stood too, and we walked out of the room. He went to the right, and I went to the left.

"See you tomorrow," Dr. Smithson said as he walked down the hallway.

I went back to my room, resumed my position on the bed and stared out the window. "Will I find answers here?" I wondered.

"Time for lunch!"

A big black man knocked on my door. He stood about six foot-three and weighed two hundred and fifty pounds or more. With a bald head and a beard with a gold earring in his left ear, he appeared intimidating.

"Huh?" I replied.

"You gonna' go have some lunch with us?" There were more guys standing in the hall waiting.

"Sure, man. Let's go!" I swung quickly out of the bed and walked to the door.

"I'm Theo." He extended his hand to me.

"Eric. Nice to meet you." I shook his hand.

"Hi, I'm Bill," he was about five-eight, slight build and curly red hair.

"I'm Kurt." He looked like he had just come from a dog fight. Dirty T-shirt, uncombed hair and soiled jeans.

"I'm Wally," an obese good ole boy with a Southern twang. He had long black hair that had not been washed in a few days. A front tooth was missing.

"Eric, Eric Crane." Having shook everyone's hand, we walked down the hallway toward the cafeteria.

"We don't use last names here, Eric. Everybody goes by first name only." Bill spoke as we walked down the corridor toward the cafeteria.

"Just got here, huh?" Wally was behind me.

"Yep. This morning. I guess they think I'm pretty bad off." We turned the corner to go down another hallway.

"Don't matter what they think. What you think's what matters most around here." Theo spoke with authority.

"Well, let's say I don't really know for sure what I think. I guess I'm in the right place. I probably don't want to accept it I suppose."

"Page four-forty-nine." Wally said in a know it all tone.

"What?" I replied, not having a clue about what he said.

"Page four-forty-nine of the Big Book. Acceptance."

Theo took up for me. "Hey Wally, he don't know nothing about the Big Book. Let up, man."

"That's okay," I said. "Guess I do know why I'm here. It's just not where I'd planned to be at this point in my life."

Bill chimed in. "Yeah, I know what you mean, man. All my best thinking in life got me to Peachtree Institute."

"Here's the cafeteria!" Wally exclaimed.

Mystery meat, mystery salad, mystery vegetables and pink lemonade, tea or water. "I better leave a good tip," I joked with my new friends.

"It don't get no better than this," cracked Wally with a grin. "You'll be hopping to the head tonight!"

We ate lunch and went back to the Unit. The next event for the day was a two-hour group session. I went into the group room and found a seat next to Theo. Eleven others came in plus a therapist named Eddie.

"Good afternoon, everyone. Let's start by going around and introducing ourselves by our first name and our diagnosis and tell us how you feel today."

"I'm Pamela, and I'm an alcoholic and manic-depressive. I feel okay."

"I'm Lawrence, and I'm a drug addict and depressed, and I feel tired."

They continued around. I stopped listening and wondered what I should say when they got to me. Was I an alcoholic?

"Your turn, man." Theo elbowed me. The moment had come. Abliel and Vida had told me to follow my Truth. They said to be honest about everything. There I was, after all my efforts at living the good life, in a room full of drug addicts and alcoholics on a Wednesday afternoon. "Crane, you have definitely arrived," I thought. Oh well, here goes.

"My name is Eric, and I uh, I uh, well I guess I'm an alcoholic, too." There, I had said it. Mr. Eric Crane admitted he was an alcoholic in front of the entire world. Now everyone knew it, and it was out in the open.

To my surprise, everyone looked at me and said nothing. Finally someone said, "What's your other diagnosis?"

It had taken all my nerve to say I was an alcoholic and the only thing these people wanted to know was my other diagnosis. I mean, "Come on, people, don't you know who I am? I'm Eric Crane, and I've just admitted that I'm an alcoholic!" Didn't anyone get it?

"Yeah, man, what's your other diagnosis?" asked Kurt.

"Eric just got here and he doesn't know yet," Eddie replied. "Let's continue."

They completed the introductions, and I sat there dumfounded. No one cared that I was an alcoholic. These people didn't know me until that day, and they didn't care. They did not want anything from me, nor did they expect anything from me. I was free to be whoever I wanted to be there. I could be a rock star, a movie actor, the President, it did not matter. I was there and was part of the group.

What a relief. I had admitted my alcoholism, and I was okay. No one said anything about it. It was a safe place to be. I felt like a million tons of pressure had been lifted off my shoulders. I had been honest and found a way to speak my truth.

The group finally finished, and I went to my room. A blue book had been placed upon my bed called "Alcoholics Anonymous." I picked it up and thumbed through it. The pages fell open to page eighty-four where I started to read. There they were again, the same words I had read on the poster in the admitting office that morning! *If we are painstaking about …*

I kept reading. I turned to the front and read a story about a guy named Bill and his spiritual awakening that instantaneously transformed his way of life. He described how he went from a state of hopelessness to one of pure hope. He had experienced the love of the Father of Light in each of us. He had found a power greater than himself and by giving himself completely to that power, he was able to stop drinking, and he found peace and serenity.

Bill's story spoke to me. Something about it clicked. He had felt like I did, and he found a way out. Bill had found the answer. I always wanted to find the answer, but it seemed the harder I looked, the more lost I became. In my hands was the story of a guy who had gotten so buried by life he had lost all hope, but something happened at his moment of hopelessness. He quit fighting. He was defeated and had nothing left inside to give. In this utter despair he found a solution.

"Sound familiar?" a voice came from the back corner of the room.

"Vida, long time, no see!"

"You've been doing quite well on your own, Eric." He took the chair, moved it in front of me and sat in it.

"Yeah, and look where I am. The funny farm!"

"You are where you are." He shrugged his shoulders.

"Thanks. Thanks a lot." I looked away.

"Do you understand the principle behind Bill's story?"

"Principle? I thought he found the answer through a spiritual awakening."

"True. However, there is more than that in what he found. There are certain principles, or laws, that work behind the scenes."

I looked at Vida as I had so many times before, in utter amazement. I suppose by then he had come to understand my blank stare that said, "Help me out here, Vida."

So, he did. "To get anywhere, to find any hope of any answer, Bill first had to be honest and admit he had no answer, that he had no more fuel inside of him and that the things he had been doing had not worked. That moment required that he be honest to himself; so honest he was willing to accept any consequence of what was to come next."

I wasn't sure if I was getting it or not. Vida continued. "He had to lay aside the False Center that ruled him. He had to allow life to lead him to his True Center. Through honesty, he came to understand that his way of living life had made him unhappy and hopeless. He needed to be at a turning point, his crossroads. He needed complete and total honesty. By that, I mean he could not hold onto even one part of his old way of thinking that kept him in his false self, or his False Center."

Now it was making sense. Vida stretched his legs and leaned back.

"Honesty in that form transcends all the defenses you build up from years of denial. You go through life denying to the outside that nothing's wrong on the inside. In truth, nothing is right on the inside. You have used up your energy in lies about your state of mind. You have manipulated your world to suit your desires, but in the end, you finally discover you have no more power to manipulate, no more power to control, and no more power to continue. By the principle of honesty, you must admit you have lost the race, lost the answer, lost your power. That's when your answer appears."

"But I thought I was honest," I said, then I rationalized to myself, "I had been up to then, right?"

"Eric, you believe you are honest, and that's the number-one stumbling block, the ultimate form of deception. The big lie is your Ego saying to you, "It's not that bad, you're okay. It's the other guy's fault." You are convinced that you are still in control, that there is nothing wrong with your thinking. The truth is you haven't got a clue about what it truly means to be honest with yourself. You live in a delusion that you are right."

I did not want to hear that. I wanted to fight back, to defend myself. But the fact remained, my life was falling apart and I was emotionally out of gas. Bill's story, in the Big Book, hit home. I wanted what he had. "So what do I do?" Vida stood.

"Listen to your True Center, Eric. We have been over this ground before. Listen. Simply go within and listen to your Truth. Your Truth will always lead you to your Good." With that, Vida winked at me and left my room.

He had given me much to contemplate. My Truth. What did my Truth have to say? What would it take to really be honest. "What did I have to admit?" I silently asked myself.

Somewhere in the recess of my mind the word "Acceptance" was heard.

"That's it!" I thought. I needed to accept where I was. Acceptance of who I was and where I was held the key! I needed to accept that my actions had led me to the end of the street. I had used my most brilliant thinking and planning in my life, only to end up in the treatment center. I had to admit to the core of my being that I had been beaten up and I had no more power to continue down the same path. I needed to admit that my way was not working, and that I had made a mess of my life.

I thought, "Okay, I admit I'm an alcoholic. I accept the fact that my way of living hasn't worked out, and I'm out of gas. I admit I need help, that I can't carry the weight any more. I give up. I have a problem and I have no solution."

At that moment, at the point that I finally accepted this stark reality, I felt an instant relief. I had no idea where I was going with it, nor thoughts of what was to happen next, but I felt an inner release, like I had opened a bird cage and said to the captive, "Okay, you're free!"

Theo knocked on the door frame. "Hey man, you gonna go to dinner?"

"Is it time already?" I quickly brought my mind back to the room and looked at my watch. Five-thirty. I usually had dinner at eight o'clock at home.

"You get used to it." Theo replied.

I got up and walked out into the corridor. Kurt and Wally joined us as we left the unit and headed toward the cafeteria. There I was, walking with three guys I had not known just twenty-four hours earlier, and I felt like we were close friends. We had a connection. An honest connection.

– *Eleven* –

THE SOUL STIRS SLOWLY IN THE MORNING. PERHAPS IT HAS TRAVELED TO places unknown in the night. Weary from its sojourn, it returns to the physical realm to again assume its place of learning in what we call earth life.

Some days, we feel as if the world we left in our dreams is the world to which we belong. Those are the times when we question the life we live and wonder if our past decisions were the correct ones that will move us forward.

At those introspective moments, we are able to hear, ever so intuitively, the prompting of the quiet whisper of a voice we call Spirit. It's a familiar voice, one without audible tones, but clear, nonetheless, beyond any doubting mind. It is a voice that calls us to ourselves, to unite us with the ever-present oneness of the forces of nature, the forces of the Universe, the single ultimate force many refer to as God.

In those quiet moments during the start of a new day, when the sun is just below the horizon, putting the finishing touches on the day preceding in remote places of the world, we can unite ourselves with the mystic, ethereal self within and return to a state of being that existed before this lifetime.

It was such a morning that found me awake in the darkness of the pre-dawn, returning from a flight in the night from some far off place that can only be visited by the soul. I had a feeling, which was more than a hunch, that I had been somewhere and returned. I felt confused about where I was when I awoke.

I sat up in my bed and looked out into the darkness of my room, searching for some clue, for some familiar sign that would comfort me in knowing where I was. I saw my blue denim shirt hanging on the back of the chair where I had thoughtlessly placed it the night before, my shoes lay next to the desk, one pointing toward the wall, and the other toward the window.

Out the window I saw light from the utility pole that stood by the driveway that led to the hospital parking lot. It occurred to me, I was still in room 202 at the treatment center.

That morning, a quiet hush enveloped the unit as everyone else slept. In that moment, I felt something I had not felt in this incarnation.

It was a profound sense that something was different deep within me. The shift occurred since the night had begun. Something had changed, though I did not quite know what it was. I sensed peace that morning. As hard as I try, words cannot fully describe what I felt. Peace seems too light. Joy; too simple. Assurance; too shallow. It was more like reunion. Reunion with a part of myself that I had long forgotten along life's way, a part of me that I had disowned. That morning, however, I had awakened to a sense of gratitude that finally, part of me had been reclaimed.

Words were not required, although, at some level, communication within had occurred, for I knew there had been a change in consciousness, a quickening, that can only be experienced through communion with life at a higher plane.

I knew I was being transformed that morning to hear a new song, to listen to a new melody that could not be heard with ears, but with the heart. Something about the air around me was different than the air of the day before, as if the room itself had been transported to a place in the heavens, to a new world, free from the limits of my mortal mind. I was in a place where my soul was free to travel at will, where thought was not bound by words nor held captive by the limits of a spoken language.

I sensed unseen entities in my room that morning. They were loving, healing and pure. I felt a powerful sense of unconditional love that descended upon me like a gentle spring rain, a presence of love as real as the air I breathed. I felt as though everything I had done wrong in my life had never occurred, and that I was accepted at a level of pure being.

As I sat in my bed I uttered a humming musical sound. One note, one sound, and constant. It began quietly as a thought that slowly became audible. It gradually got louder, until I was aware of it, but it never got louder than was necessary for my ears to hear. Then it stopped.

I closed my eyes and my head listed to one side. I felt as though I was in the presence of a being of clear Light and radiant Love. The Light was crystal clear, though not a physical light, but a lightness of presence. The feeling of Love was tangibly real, though not a love that one experiences at the human level. With my eyes closed, I found myself feeling renewed, recharged, as if I had plugged into the energy connection of the Universe.

I sat for some time and then I heard words I will never forget, words that had an impact on me and changed my understanding of the relationship between man and his Creator.

I had thought all my life that God was in the sky, an old man with long white hair, a white beard and white flowing robes. I feared that God, because I felt sure he would punish me for all the wrong things I did in my life. Every thought outside of ones that were acceptable to him had been recorded, only to be re-played on that fateful day when "the roll is called up yonder."

Yet that morning changed all of that. On that morning, I discovered a Presence that was nothing like the one I grew up with and feared for so many years. On that morning, Truth was revealed to me in a moment during which I felt no fear, no judgment or criticism, but pure Love. I had felt the connection to the presence of One who was there, and had been there even before the foundation of the world. I felt the presence of One from whom I had hidden under my False Center. I felt the presence of the One Presence, the One Being, the One Source of all creation, the Presence of the One Universal God.

I had not set out to feel that Presence that evening. I had not asked in any particular act of prayer, or otherwise, that the Presence be revealed to me. But by morning, I had awakened to the Presence, and I could not ignore it, nor could I escape from the words that came so clearly: "Be still and know that I am God."

The same words Carla had read to me several days earlier were repeated over and over, and then they were spoken with a special emphasis on each word.

"Be still and know that I am God." God, the ultimate Presence in the Universe. The One Reality, the One Being in whom we have our creation and our life. God, the omnipresent One who is all life, the omniscient One who is all Intelligence, the omnipotent One who is all Power. The One Mind of the Universe from whom come all thoughts and all matter that has ever been created.

"Be still and know that I AM ..." I AM. That is who God is. I AM that I AM. Those sacred words were spoken to Moses from the burning bush on the mount. I AM. The description of our personal divinity as God's creations. I AM, the place of divine life, eternal spirit, and everlasting love that God placed in every being since the beginning. The essence of Good and Love. The absolute knowing that the Father and I are indeed One.

"Be still and know ..." We can know, and it was for me to know, that there is One Presence in the Universe and it wasn't a traffic cop waiting for me to make a wrong turn and then throw me into a lake of fire. I was to know and to have knowledge of this God, of this Presence, the One Reality of all creation. I had the privilege of knowing and from knowledge springs hope. By knowing, I could trust there is purpose in the otherwise seemingly senseless lessons experienced in this mortal incarnation. I had been in the fire, yet I was not consumed. That I knew. The presence of the One Power in my life had seen me through it, and was now restoring me to sanity.

"Be still ..." It was only by being still on that morning that I was able to hear the words, to sense the Presence, to have a sacred experience with the One God. Only after I had admitted defeat from the internal war that had been raging in my soul for many years, could I be still enough to feel Love from the One True Presence. Admitting my human-ness and letting go of the notion that I had to be perfect, meant I no longer needed to play god, that I no longer had to run life on my limited source of Ego-power. I could be still. I could surrender and rest. I could stop fighting against the unknown enemy and let the One True Source of Life flow from my True Center and thus grant me Abundant Life.

"Be ..." I could simply be who I was. Down, broken, defeated and out of gas, I could lay down my weapons of personal destruction; my addictions, my obsessions, and I could be the pure Soul I was created to be. I had no need for pretense, no need for show. I had no need to live out a role that was unlivable, to accept the unacceptable, to believe the unbelievable. I was at a place where the One God of the Universe was saying to me "It is all right; just be the individual I have created you to be." That was all I could be. I was Eric, and as Eric, I was accepted as a divine child, through the power of Love, into the presence of a loving God, who was incapable of judging me, a God who could do no more nor no less than love me as His child.

In the moment of that morning in my hospital room, all was changed in the twinkling of an eye. It seemed that time and space ceased to exist, and the world finally stopped, so I could be in the Presence. I had no place to go, no thing I had to do, no role I had to play. In that moment in my room I was simply there, in the moment appointed for me.

That moment was all that was required. That was my moment for my God and me to be reunited. In that moment when there was no sound, when there was no movement, when there was no activity, God revealed Himself to me as a kind, loving being that knew me intimately.

In all the moments of my life until that moment, I had not been ready to experience the presence of God as I did then. I had been too busy or too anxious or too whatever I was at the time, to hear the still, quiet voice within. I was always trying to understand on my own terms, in my own limited thoughts and preconceived ideas of who God was and how He should be sought.

When I finally came to the point in my life when living did not seem worthwhile, when all my efforts seemed to have been for naught, when all the pushing for status in the world had come to an end, I found God's Presence in my life.

I had fooled myself for years into limited thinking, into false ideas and into solutions from the outside. I had given myself to the world and to the cycle of insanity that comes from repeating the same behaviors, while expecting different results.

I had run a million miles an hour and had pushed the envelope as far as I could, and when there was no more push, I made one final futile attempt to make everything turn out my way.

Once my path had taken what I thought was a turn for the worse, when I had given up all hope, had given up the belief that I was the director of the show, I found the answer I desperately tried to find all my life.

My God, the True Essence of all Life, dwelt within me, and had been there all the time.

As the sun rose slowly above the horizon, the birds of spring began their morning songs of light and praise. Out in the hall, I heard the nurses' conversation, though the words were unintelligible. In my room there was Light where there once was darkness. There was hope where there once was despair. There was a feeling of connectedness where there once was a feeling of being alone.

One moment was all the transformation took, one moment in all the moments of eternity. The God of the Universe had set aside that one moment for Eric Crane to know he was not alone, that he was on the right Path, that his life had purpose.

All I could say after that moment was one word. I felt as though any word was insufficient for a moment like that, and there was only one word that felt appropriate.

What do you say to a moment like that? What can you say when the Creator of Love reveals Himself to you? What can you say when there is nothing left to say?

My insides pumped tears of a new joy to my eyes. I shook in awe and humility as I attempted to say the one word which, as a human, was the only word I could say after a moment like that. "Thank-you."

– *Twelve* –

Lee Sanchez, the clinical social worker assigned to my case, must have been in her mid fifties. She had salt-and-pepper hair, cut short, right above the collar line. On her desk were photographs of what I believed to be her family. In one, a young female wore a cap and gown. Another featured a young male in an Army uniform. On the end was a photo of a younger Lee and a man, heads tilted toward one another, arm in arm with expressions of happiness and love. I guessed that he was her husband.

Lee wore a wedding band and a diamond that looked like it might have been half a carat. She dressed modestly. That day she sported a dark blue skirt and a maroon-and-white striped shirt. Her only other jewelry was her watch and gold earrings.

"Please have a seat, Mr. Crane." She motioned me to her couch. The office reminded me of Amy Carlson's, nice and homelike in appearance and feeling. Lee took a seat in a comfortable-looking upholstered chair and propped up her feet on a small footstool.

"So how are you getting along here at Peachtree?"

"It's not bad. In fact, it feels good to take a breather." I chuckled.

"A breather?" She had a curious smile on her face.

"Yeah, you know, like in basketball; I'm sitting on the bench for a breather. Like I've put my world in neutral for a few weeks. It feels good to be able to do that." I waved my hands to describe what I was saying.

"Does that mean this isn't real to you?"

"Oh it's very real, it's just that I don't have any responsibilities while I'm in here. You know, there's nothing I can do about anything out there," I pointed to the window, "while I'm in here."

"And what are you doing in here?" She smiled pleasantly.

"I'm taking it all in, as much as I can. I figure that I'm in here for a reason, so I'm putting my trust in the medical professionals who are treating me."

"Do you feel like it's doing any good?"

I thought for a brief moment. "Yes, I do feel like it's doing some good. I feel relaxed - "

"And you're taking a breather?" she interrupted. "Mr. Crane, would you mind telling me about yourself?"

For the past few days, I had spent ample time reviewing my life. Fortunately, or unfortunately, Lee Sanchez was about to hear it all. I told her about my teenage years, my marriage to Michele, my brief affair with Donna, the divorce, moving to Atlanta, how I met Sonnie and how I arrived at Peachtree.

She was attentive. "That's truly an amazing story." She made some notes, paused and looked up saying: "Tell me about your job."

"My job. I'm the vice president of a small computer software business. We develop and sell commercial grade business software to medium and large businesses."

"How long have you been doing that?"

"All totaled, I've been in the business fifteen years, or there abouts."

"You've had more than one job during that time?"

"Yeah." I counted them in my mind. "Three."

"I see." She kept making notes. "Do you enjoy your work?"

"I did at one time, but not now. I feel like I'm not making a difference. I call it pushing the rope. It takes a lot of effort, with little or no results."

"Pushing the rope. That's a new one. What's that feel like?" she flipped her note paper over to write on the other side.

"Heavy. Heavy and hard. Sometimes impossible."

"Why do you keep doing it?"

"Ha!" She must not have read the file. "I have significant child support obligations, a house payment, car payments, bills, do I need to say more?"

"So you do it because of your obligations and responsibilities?"

"That's right. I have to keep my nose to the grindstone." I was sarcastic, but I chortled nonetheless.

"That's funny?"

"Maybe not." Therapists seem to take everything I say literally.

"Mr. Crane, if there was anything you could do for a living if you did not have those obligations, what would you do?"

I had never thought about that before. I always had obligations. I had been in debt since I was a teenager, when I took out my first loan to buy a motorcycle. "I don't know, right offhand."

"Have you ever had a dream?"

"A dream? Sure. When I was a kid, I thought I would become a minister. I always thought that was what I would do. I even went to college to study for the ministry." I stopped. That's where the dream ended.

"Then what happened?" She appeared to be really interested.

"I met Michele and joined the Mormon church. They don't have paid clergy. It's a lay ministry."

"So what did you do?"

My voice became quieter. "I quit my studies and joined the business world."

"And that's not fun?"

Silence; then, "No."

More silence. Lee Sanchez continued taking notes, and said, "Tell me about things at home."

Home. I didn't want to talk about that. I thought for a moment before I spoke. "What would you like to know?"

"How about you and your wife. Her name is," she shuffled back through the paperwork in the file, "Elizabeth?"

"Sonnie. She goes by Sonnie." I spelled it for her.

"Sonnie." Lee wrote herself a note. "Okay, tell me about you and Sonnie. How long have you been married?"

"Almost five years."

"And how did you two meet?"

"She was an accountant at the company where I work. From the moment I saw Sonnie, I was turned on."

"So she looked attractive to you?"

"Attractive? It was instant lust. We started dating, and then moved in together."

"You were divorced from your first wife?"

"Not completely. I mean, we had filed for the divorce, but it wasn't final."

"Tell me more about Sonnie. Was it confusing to you?"

"How do you mean?"

"You met her, started having sex, moved in together, all while you were in the middle of a divorce from a wife of thirteen years. Not only that, but you had just relocated from Spokane where you had been in an affair. Were you confused about any of this?"

I was beginning to get confused from her questions. "Well I suppose when you put it like that, yeah, I guess I was a little mixed-up now that I look back on it." My voice grew quiet again.

"But you kept dating Sonnie. How did you end things with, let me see," she was looking through Dr. Smithson's notes in the file.

"Donna?" I attempted to be helpful.

"Let's see, oh, yes, that's right, her name is Donna. How did you end that?"

"On the telephone. I called her up and said it was no use keeping the relationship up; after all she was out there and I was here. It was impracticable." I chose not to tell her about the scene at Donna's where she had another guy over.

"So that was how it ended?" Lee asked in disbelief.

"Yeah, pretty much. Things were going good with Sonnie, so I figured there was no use in keeping Donna waiting, so I cut it off." I gazed out her office window.

"Just cut it off. Like she was a limb on a tree, you just cut it off, because — ?" She waited for me to finish her sentence.

I looked back at her. "It was a mutual thing."

"How do you know?"

"She agreed it wasn't going to work."

"Did she have someone else by that time?"

She figured it out. "Yep." I confessed reluctantly.

Lee looked at her notes and wrote something. "Let's get back to you and Sonnie. So you met and moved in together. I asked you if you were ever confused about that decision, and you said you were confused a little bit. What did you do to get clear?" She looked up at me for an answer.

What had I done to get clear? How did I get to a point that I made a decision that, in retrospect, looked stupid? I shrugged my shoulders as I had no answer.

"How much were you drinking by that time?"

"Uh, I don't know. Scotch in the evening, maybe three or four."

"Every night?"

"Yeah, pretty much."

"And the weekends, how much did you drink during the weekends?"

"A lot, I suppose."

"What's a lot?" Lee was intent with her questions.

"Sonnie and I would go out to dinner. We would have a drink or two at home before we went out, a couple of drinks at the bar while we waited for our table to be ready, a bottle of wine with dinner, after-dinner drinks, and a night cap or two when we got home."

"Was that it for the weekend?"

"No, that was for one night. For instance, on Friday night, we might have a couple of six packs with the neighbors; and on Sunday, I would have a six pack or two for the football game, or whatever else we were doing."

"Did you and Sonnie always drink like that?"

"Yep. Always. Sometimes more."

"More?" Her eyes got big.

"We liked to party." I chuckled.

"Sounds like it," Lee said. "You mentioned something about instant lust. Tell me about that."

"Sonnie and I had incredible sex. She knows how to please a man, sexually. She wears clothing that makes her look hot, and I get really turned on. We had sex every day for a long time."

"Then it tapered off?"

"Yeah. It did." I spoke in a quieter voice.

"And how is it now?"

"Well, we, we sort of have separate bedrooms, and we don't have sex very often."

"I see. You work together, but sleep separately?"

"We don't work together anymore," I admitted.

"Oh, when did that happen?"

"A few months after we started living together."

"Why did she stop working there?"

"Image. We were sending the wrong message to the other employees."

"And what was that?" Lee held her pen to her face.

"That it was all right to sleep with someone you work with."

"I see." She made some more notes.

"So now you sleep in separate beds, and you've been married five years. Does that seem strange to you?"

"Yes. Now that I hear it from you, it does sound strange."

"So the marriage isn't going too well at this point?" Her statement took the form of a question.

"I guess not." I got quiet again.

"Okay. Let's stop here for today. I will see you again, and Mrs. Crane, too, if you don't mind." She closed my file.

I considered it, "No, no I don't mind. I suppose this is when we should do it."

"Great. I'll call her and see what we can arrange. Thanks for your time." Lee stood up and offered me her hand.

"Thank you." I stood. We shook hands and I left, headed for room 202.

Lee Sanchez had put something into perspective for me. My choice to be married to Sonnie was made during a time of confusion and turmoil. The fact that we were sleeping in separate bedrooms was apparently symptomatic of a deeper problem. I would have preferred not to address the issue.

Room 202 became my sanctuary, my new 'cave.' It was different than the dark cave of my dream where I was in shackles. It was a safe cave, where I was able to summon courage in facing my challenges. In that room I discovered my Higher Power, which made room 202 a holy place for me. Nothing aesthetic about the room made it more conducive to discovering a Higher Power than other rooms. I didn't burn incense, no pictures hung from the walls, no sculptures adorned the table, nothing other than institutional paint and linoleum floors. Yet, there in room 202 I had one of life's most profound experiences.

"Because you are allowing these things to occur here." Vida's voice was unmistakable.

"Vida!" I turned around to greet my mentor.

"Hello, Eric. Your path has brought you to a place you would never have chosen to come, and now, look at what you've discovered already."

"You're right again. Of all the places I could have gone to experience God's Presence, a secluded beach, a mountain top, a hike in the forest. Who could have imagined I would find God here."

"It's not the place, it's the person. When we become ready, we will receive the lesson." Vida walked past me to take a seat on the other bed. "You have been preparing yourself to meet your Higher Power. As you continue on your path, this relationship will become increasingly more important. Eventually, you will not need me."

"Not need you?" I sat up on my bed.

"When you find your True Center, you are connected directly to the Source of All There Is. The need for a Spirit Guide lessens."

"But even if I am connected to the Source, can't I still visit with you?" Vida had become more than a friend. Without him, I would be hopelessly lost. I didn't want to lose him.

"Sure, you always have the choice to seek guidance from me, Abliel and others, but you may prefer to get your direction directly. Besides, we're not at that point in your development. What you need to know now is that you have found your Higher Power. You need to know that you can be in the presence of this Power at any time, no matter what. When you experience pain from personal growth, you will come to find strength and comfort in the presence of this Power."

"But how do I do it?" I held out my hand.

"The same way you did it before. Be still." With that Vida stood up, touched my shoulder, and walked back the way he came in, and was gone.

"Be still," I thought. That's how it happened before. That's how it will happen again.

Theo was knocking on the door. "Time for lunch."

"Already?" I stood, and we walked to the cafeteria.

"I had a meeting with my social worker." I casually remarked to Theo.

"Oh yeah? How'd it go?" We turned a corner.

"Not bad. It's caused me to think about my wife and me."

"Yeah, it'll do that for sure, man." Theo spoke like someone who had experienced the same thing. "My old lady, she ain't too happy with me, but she says she's gonna stay with me and see this thing through."

"That's great Theo! I hope Sonnie feels the same way." We got to the cafeteria line. "Let's see what the chef has for us today. Ah, turkey and dressing. Yum, yum." I rubbed my stomach for effect.

"Beats what I was eating before I came here though," Theo picked up his tray and moved down the line. "That dumpster food was always cold." He laughed.

We got our plates and drinks and found our way to a table.

"My doctor says I'll be going home soon." Theo put a fork full of food in his mouth.

"Oh yeah?" In just a few days, Theo had become a close friend. He was black and lived in project housing; I was white and lived in an affluent suburb. In spite of socio-economic differences, we had found a common thread; humanness. It saw none of the outside things that separated us.

Our humanness brought us together, made us one and liberated our seeing, our listening and our speaking so that we could transcend our programmed responses to those who were "different." When we netted everything out, the only differences were in our minds. We both held prejudices; we both had preconceived ideas about who and what the other guy should be. We both had to get over it and see each other as equals.

We chit chatted over lunch and decided to take a walk around the grounds. We got passes from the nurses station attendant, exited the doors and walked down the sidewalk.

"So, you're going to get to go home and be with your wife?" I asked.

"Yeah, man. And I'm kinda scared too, you know what I mean?"

"Sort of." I lied. I really did not know how he felt.

"I'm thinking that seeing her might make me want to use again. We like to party." Theo's voice was apprehensive.

"Yeah, party on, dude!" I tried to lighten things up.

"So, what should I do?" Theo looked at me, as he asked.

"A friend of mine told me that fear comes as a result of thinking ahead of yourself. We project our life into the future, imagining events that may not take place. He suggested that when I found myself in that mode, to bring my thoughts back to the present."

"Hmm. Ain't heard it said like that before." He rubbed his goat-tee.

"Me either, but it makes sense, and I've been trying it while I'm here."

"Does it work?"

"Yeah. Seems to."

"Maybe I'll give it a try." We turned and walked by the basketball court.

"Hell, Theo, maybe she's found another man while you've been in here." I decided to inject some humor into the conversation.

"That's just what I needed to hear, man." Theo took a friendly jab at me that landed on my arm. I returned one. It's a guy way of bonding.

We continued our walk for about ten more minutes, and returned to the wing for afternoon group. The topic was the Second Step:

Came to believe that a Power greater than ourselves could restore us to sanity.

Lisa, the facilitator, was an attractive woman in her twenties. She didn't look like an alcoholic, but then what did I know? I didn't think I looked like an alcoholic, yet there I was, in a room with fifteen other alcoholics. Some looked it, and others didn't. We went around the circle and all the participants introduced themselves in the usual manner. There were two new people, an older woman named Bessie and a young guy named Leon.

Lisa said, "I'm going to pass out a worksheet for the Second Step. I want you to work on it during the next two days. This Step is important because it sets the foundation for our recovery; a Power greater than ourselves." Lisa finished handing out the worksheets and had taken her seat.

"Does anyone have anything they'd like to say regarding Step Two?" She paused and looked around the group while she waited for someone to raise a hand. No one did, so she continued to speak.

"You know a Power greater than ourselves is what we refer to as our Higher Power, and this can be anything you like. Some people call this Power 'HP,' some call it 'God' and others call it whatever works for them.

"In the past, alcohol was my Higher Power. I turned to it for comfort and strength, but eventually that didn't work anymore for me, and I had to find another Higher Power. I tried men and sex, but those, too, had no lasting effect. It wasn't until I came into the Program that I was finally able to find a Higher Power that works for me. Now, after five years of recovery, I've found that my Higher Power is always there for me. All I have to do is go to It, be in Its presence, and I'm restored or comforted."

Someone raised her hand.

"Keena."

"I don't know 'bout no God stuff. I've had that preached at me all my life, and I don't want to hear no more 'bout God."

"That's right," I heard a few people echo quietly.

"Okay, God doesn't have to be your Higher Power. You can choose something else. Is there something that has more power than you?"

Wally raised his hand. "My Harley has more power than me!" He laughed. Everyone else did too.

"If you believe your Harley can restore you to sanity, then your Harley can be your Higher Power." Lisa was confident. "Who else?"

"The ocean," Bill added. "Whenever I go to the ocean, I feel good, and it's damn sure stronger than me."

"That's great, Bill! The ocean can be your Higher Power. The sound of the ocean can be soothing, and if it can restore you to sanity, then it can be your Higher Power."

I raised my hand.

"Eric."

"I'm not sure I know what sanity is. I've felt like my entire life has been insane. As a child, I was physically abused in the name of discipline. I never knew when or why I was going to get a beating. It was crazy. As a teenager, I used drugs and drank a lot of alcohol. Things were crazy at that time too. As an adult, I've never been very happy. Life's been a miserable event for me. How can I be restored to sanity, if I've never experienced it?"

"That's a good question. You will have to find sanity through the help of your Higher Power. No one can hand it to you. Through the help of the Twelve Steps, you may find you have experienced moments of sanity along the way. You will definitely come to a place of freedom and happiness if you really work the Steps." Lisa never hesitated. She seemed totally assured. She had something I wanted, a sense of conviction. Her face expressed serenity, and she smiled often. I decided to go along with her because if what she said was true, I was willing to work for it.

I spent the next couple of days in group therapy discussing the diseases of alcoholism and depression. Because I suffered from both, I was eager to learn all I could about the two. We heard a lecture from the head of Psychiatry, Dr. Johnson. I took copious notes as he spoke.

"We think nothing of taking insulin for diabetes if the pancreas cannot make enough on its own. If our vision is poor, we correct it with glasses or contact lenses. But when our brain doesn't generate the proper amount of neurotransmitters we are reluctant to take medication. We do so only as a last resort, when we realize that optimistic thinking, or other self styled efforts cannot correct it.

"Depression is seen as some kind of personal weakness, when in fact, it is a physiological condition. Would you let a weak heart go untreated? Why then, would you ignore another organ and let it continue in a diseased state? We call that particular organ a brain, but when it doesn't work right, that doesn't mean you failed anymore than you fail if you have diabetes. It's simply the way things are.

"The good news is that depression is a disease. What we mean is that it has observable symptoms, that many of you have experienced; irritability, sleeplessness, fatigue, having no fun, lack of concentration, crying a lot, not wanting to get out of bed in the morning, little things overwhelm you and so on.

"Because depression is a disease, it is treatable. Through proper medication, we can correct the deficiencies of the brain and bring it back to what we think of as normal. From there, it's up to you. We recommend psychotherapy in combination with medication.

"Alcoholics have a complication where depression is concerned. Alcohol is a depressant. All of the years you've been drinking, you've increased the problem. It's like you have been pouring gasoline on a fire. You may require additional therapy, such as electroshock to stimulate the brain.

"That treatment is rare, though, and is used only as a last resort. Ninety-five percent of all diagnosed cases of depression are treatable through proper medication. The key is to have the correct diagnosis, because there are several forms of the disease."

He continued to explain it to us in layman's terms. I appreciated that. He helped me understand what was going on with me in a physiological sense. Later in the day, I met with Dr. Smithson in one of the patient interview rooms.

"How are you doing today, Mr. Crane?" Dr. Smithson always called me Mr. Crane. Everyone else called me Eric. I called him Dr. Smithson.

"Good," I replied.

"Have you learned anything new?"

"I think so. What type of depression do you think I have?" I couldn't wait for his answer.

"You have two forms of depression. One is what we call Major Clinical Depression, and the other is Dysthymia. The latter is a long-term, low-grade depression that lasts for years. In your case, it has probably been around since adolescence. The first type, Major Depression, usually is more short term. It can be triggered by a shock to the nervous system or to the body in general. Life circumstances can also trigger it, especially with someone like you who suffers from Dysthymia and alcoholism. How are you sleeping?" He asked.

"Not, very well. It takes a long time to fall asleep and I wake up several times in the night."

"Okay, I'm going to increase your medication, and add something to help you sleep. I want you to take all your medications at night. Any questions?" He wrote some notes, put his pen in his pocket and closed the file.

"Yes. I've had a session with the social worker. How long will that last?"

"Is it helpful?" He looked up.

"I think so."

"Let's go for every other day for the rest of the week and then look at it again, okay?"

"Okay."

"Anything else?" He returned his pen to his shirt pocket.

"No thanks. That's it for now."

"Fine." He stood up and offered his hand. "I'll talk to you tomorrow." We shook hands and walked out the interview room. He went his way, and I went back to room 202.

Theo knocked on the door. "Hey man, I just stopped by to say good-bye." He held a duffel bag in his left hand and wore a Falcons jacket.

"You're leaving already?" Anxiety ripped through my gut.

"Yeah. Get to go home and be with my wife. The party's over."

"Wow. I had forgotten that today was the day." I walked over to Theo. He dropped his duffel bag, held out his big arms, and we embraced.

I can't recall embracing a man like that, but then, having a friend like Theo was unusual for me. He had extended himself to me from the first day of treatment. Without knowing me from a hole in the wall, he offered his friendship to me. Over the past week, we had shared things that we had not shared with another human being. We were on a path. A path to find our True Center. We held each other long enough that we both got choked up.

Beginning as quivers, emotions rushed up stronger until they trickled into a silent cry. We heard the telltale sniffles. Theo squeezed me tightly, stood there with tears flowing down his big black cheeks and said, "I love you, man."

I was speechless. "Yeah, me too. I love you too, man." I mumbled quietly.

We separated. He picked up his duffel bag, turned and slowly walked down the hall. Andy met him at the nurses' station, checked his belongings, handed him some paper, and ushered him through the doors to the wing. Halfway through Theo stopped, looked back over his shoulder to me, and gave me a thumbs up sign.

Choking back my emotions with all my strength, I looked at him and reciprocated. "Please don't forget me Theo," I silently thought.

He turned around and walked on, the doors closing behind him. I went back into room 202, stretched out on my bed, stomach down, grabbed my pillow, buried my face in it and cut loose. Sounds came from down inside. Moans, heavy moans came up as I let the torrent flow. My friend was gone.

Treatment sucks.

– *Thirteen* –

"The marriage isn't working for me anymore." Sonnie explained to Lee Sanchez. Lee was able to get Sonnie to come in for a joint session to talk about my treatment program. She had spent twenty minutes or so explaining my depression and alcoholism. She eventually got to our living in separate rooms. She had asked Sonnie why.

"Not working? What do you mean when you say, 'not working'?" Lee asked.

"Oh, you know, it just doesn't seem to be much of a marriage. I mean if you really care about someone, you don't do and say the things he does." Sonnie whined as she often did when she spoke.

"Can you give me an example?" Lee focused on Sonnie. I was curious, too. "Where was she coming from?" I wondered.

"He doesn't talk much and when he does, it's in a defensive, combative style. We don't do much anymore and, I don't know, it's just that it's not good for me. I don't feel," she paused briefly, "like I'm number one in his life."

"What do you mean about being number one?" Lee asked her.

"Eric has children from his first marriage, and whenever we have plans, they seem to get interrupted, because of something that's going on with one of them." Sonnie sat as far back into the couch as she could go as she spoke.

"I mean, I understand his children from his marriage to Michele are important, but I feel like I'm less important, like I'm supposed to put my needs on hold while they get his attention." She waved her hands about.

I sat there, a little amused and a lot pissed-off.

"So you feel as though Eric should give you some more attention?"

"Yes, I think that's true, although, I don't know if he's even capable of it." Sonnie glanced at me.

"Eric? How do you feel about all of this?" Lee Sanchez looked at me as well.

It was my turn. I could have said many things. But my anger grabbed my words and held them in my throat. It took a moment for me to gain my composure. Sonnie nervously uncrossed her legs and rearranged her position.

I finally freed my words and spoke in a controlled, deliberate manner. "I don't know what to say. I work hard to provide a certain lifestyle for Sonnie. I have child-support obligations too. It takes a lot to make everything work out. I don't know about it 'not working,' or about her not being first. I'm confused." I shook my head.

"Perhaps you can tell us how you feel right now, Eric." Lee tried to get me tuned-in to the session.

"I feel..." I paused, cleared my throat, and released control as my anger rushed out of my mouth. "I'm angry. I mean, I work pretty damn hard to make sure that she lives comfortably. We go out to eat more than I can afford to and she always wants to take trips to the beach. It's like there is never enough for her. The more I do, the more she wants. I suppose if I made a million dollars a year, that wouldn't be enough. She would always want more." I couldn't look at Sonnie. My anger boiled red inside.

"And as far as being first, what is she talking about? Why do I knock myself out, if she's not first?" My voice crescendoed. "She is first. She always wants to know if I'm having an affair, and I tell her 'no,' and that's the truth, but she doesn't believe me."

"Sonnie? Did you hear Eric?" Lee turned toward Sonnie.

"Oh yes, I heard him. I hear him all the time telling me how he is doing it all for me," She said sarcastically.

"That's not what I heard, Sonnie," Lee clarified, "I heard him say how important you are. I also heard him say that you were never satisfied. Are you?"

"Well, yes, I guess."

"He also said he was confused. Can you help him get clear about what's not working?" Lee held out her hand.

"The relationship. The marriage. It's nonexistent. I mean, how many couples do you know that sleep in different beds?" Sonnie exclaimed.

"Why do you sleep in different beds?" Lee looked puzzled.

I couldn't stand it. "Because, if I don't perform exactly as she demands, I get cut off. I can't hold her, she won't allow sex, and she won't allow me to touch her in any way." I had a lot of angry energy attached to that.

"Oh, Eric, come on. You and I both know that we sleep in different beds because of your snoring!" Sonnie retorted.

"What?" I looked at her in amazement. Sure, I had sleep apnea and it caused me to snore a lot, but I had also had surgery to correct it and she still wouldn't sleep with me unless *she* wanted sex. "That's bullshit Sonnie. You know damn good and well that's not true. The real reason is you think you're a queen, and we all better serve you, no matter what."

"Eric, you can't say something she is feeling is not true. Her feelings may not coincide with your perception of what you think reality is, but we can't judge how others see their truth." According to the clock on her desk, almost an hour had gone by. "Is there anything else you'd like to say, Sonnie?"

"Yes. First, thanks for saying that to Eric. He always wants me to agree, that what he says is right. Second, I don't want to continue in this marriage." She looked down.

Silence. I was stunned. Her remark caught me completely off guard.

"Does that mean you want a divorce?" Lee asked.

"Yes. That's what I'm saying. It's just not working anymore, and I don't see any reason to keep it going." Sonnie looked down at her hands, which she was wringing.

"I see. Eric?" Lee looked at me.

One of the symptoms of depression is crying. Depressives cry over anything. Sonnie's statement wasn't "anything", it was huge. Tears started. Theo left yesterday, and Sonnie wants to leave today. My resevoir of emotions was full. I wanted to say something, anything. I didn't want Sonnie to see me cry. Whenever I cried about something at home, she acted disgusted, as if to say "how could you cry over something like that?" However, that's how it is with depression. You cry over things that appear small to others. Still, this wasn't small. It was gigantic. Sonnie wanted out. I knew things were bad between us, but I felt they could be fixed. After all, I was in treatment, and I thought I could get on top of our problems.

And what about our children? During our five years of marriage we had two children. What about them? I looked at Lee Sanchez for help. I wanted to bolt out her door and run and hide. I stuffed my feelings down inside and said, "I have nothing to say." I managed to get that much out. I wanted to say "Go ahead. Get out of here, then, if that's how you feel! You're around when the chips are up, but when they are down, it's 'not working' for you, and off you go. Well go then, and good riddance!", but I didn't. I chose to clam up, rather than let Sonnie have the satisfaction of seeing and hearing how I truly felt. After all, she wanted a divorce.

"Well, let's leave it here for the time being and we can resume this later. Is that okay with you Sonnie?"

Sonnie nodded as she put a pleasant smile on her face.

"Eric?" Lee looked at me.

I nodded to indicate agreement and looked away as I bit my top lip.

"Eric, I'd like you to stay here for a few minutes while I walk your wife out. Would you mind?"

"No." I couldn't look at her.

Lee walked Sonnie to the door and asked if she needed help finding the main entrance. Sonnie said, "no thanks." They said good-bye and Lee returned, closing the door behind her.

"Eric, what's going on?" she leaned up against the edge of her desk.

What's going on? WHAT'S GOING ON? "I want to go. I want to get the hell out of here as fast as I can." I still could not look at her.

"I see. You want to leave?"

"I want to leave, check out, vamoose, get outta Dodge, I want to go as far away as I can!" I yelled and cried at the same time.

"What would you do if I let you go?" Lee moved over to a chair beside me and offered me some facial tissues.

"I'd get drunker than drunk. I'd check out. I'd never come back."

"What do you mean 'check out'?"

"You know, check out, turn out the lights, call it quits. Blow my brains out, that's what!" Now I was trembling and crying. I grabbed a tissue.

"You mean suicide?"

"Damn straight, that's what I mean!" My mind was like a tornado, out of control and destructive.

It is a mistake to say that you feel suicidal in a mental hospital, but that's exactly how I felt. To the mental health profession, suicide is a code blue, the ultimate crisis.

"Okay, Eric, okay. Stay right there for a moment. Lee went over to her phone and punched a button. She quietly said a few words to the person on the other end.

"This is Lee Sanchez. I have a patient in my office with ideations."

She hung up the phone and looked at me. "Eric, I know this is difficult, but you will get through it. I'm going to call Dr. Smithson. Meanwhile, you're going to be escorted to your room and placed under watch. Do you understand?" Lee walked around to the couch.

I nodded "okay." Two guys came to the door to take me to my room. When I got to the wing, Suzanne, the head nurse, stopped us.

"Dr. Smithson called special orders to take him to ICU," She said. They turned around. ICU is where the real nut cases go. If you mention even thinking about suicide, they put you in ICU.

A few minutes later we came to the ICU nurses' station. "Take him to number seven, but first he needs some meds," ordered a nurse. The two men escorted me over to a Dutch door with the top open. A nurse was inside preparing medication.

"Is this Mr. Crane?" she asked.

"Yes." Replied one of the men.

"Mr. Crane, I need you to take these."

She handed me a small white cup that had three pills in it. One was white, another was yellow and the third was pink. In the other hand, she held a paper cup of water.

"What's this for?" I asked.

"To relax you sir. Your doctor ordered it for you. You'll feel better soon."

I took the pills and washed them down with water. "It's all part of the system," I thought. "If he has a problem, give him some pills. Insurance will cover it, and everyone makes a buck." Cynicism was easy for me.

I was then escorted to room number seven. It looked like room 202, except it had only one bed in it and no window. The door was shut part way behind me as I was released into the room. I went over to the bed and fell into it, face first. I cursed as I cried again.

"Eric." It was Abliel's voice.

"Abliel?" I raised my head from the bed.

"It's all right Eric. Everything is as it should be. You will be fine." His calm voice comforted me.

"Abliel, I - I, I give up!" I buried my head again.

"That's good Eric. When one surrenders, one wins."

"Huh?" I raised up again.

"Vida will explain. We will talk later. That is all for now."

"Tough one, huh?" Vida was there.

"Yeah. I knew things weren't all that great, but the divorce bit, man, it threw me for a loop." I found a tissue and put it to use.

"How will suicide change things?" Vida asked.

"What do you mean?"

"You want out? What will be the outcome if that happens?"

I had not thought it through. All I could think about was how much I hurt. "I haven't thought about that."

"You must work *through* your lessons. No lesson is too difficult, it only appears that way sometimes. The act of suicide does not change the fact that you have a lesson to learn. If you choose to kill yourself, you will have to come back and learn the lesson in another lifetime. The negative karma created from suicide makes it a more difficult lesson to learn later.

"I realize how much you hurt, Eric. But suicide is not the answer. You must work through this in order to grow. Growth requires letting go of old ways, old patterns and sometimes, though not always, relationships that prevent your spiritual growth."

"If it's a choice between growth and Sonnie, I'd rather have Sonnie." I moved to a sitting position on the side of the bed.

Vida sat next to me. "That's a choice for you *and* Sonnie."

"Well, I know my choice. The last thing I want is a second divorce." I had told Sonnie many times over the past several years that our marriage would be my last.

"It's not entirely up to you, Eric. It takes two to make the decision to work through the tough issues of a marriage." Vida scratched the top of his head.

"So she has to want it, too?" A second tissue was fetched.

"And choose it." He sat next to me.

"Choose it?"

"A choice must be made to stay in a marriage and to work through the matters that must be worked through. Wanting it and choosing it are not the same."

I must have looked as puzzled as I felt, so he persevered.

"One may want something and still not choose to do what is required to earn or receive it. Choosing implies you have thought it through and have seen yourself in the relationship you desire and have accepted the responsibility to do what is necessary to cultivate it."

"Okay." My tone indicated I sort of understood.

"You say you don't want a divorce. Have you visualized the marriage in a harmonious state, and have you committed to spend the energy required to make it healthy?" He leaned against the wall.

"No, I haven't quite gone to that length. I've just been thinking about not having Sonnie, and that hurts like hell."

"Take a moment and try to see you and Sonnie together in a healthy relationship."

I closed my eyes and took a deep breath. In my mind, I held a picture of Sonnie and I holding one another. We were smiling and enjoying being in each other's arms. It was a picture that was reminiscent of our early days together, not the way things were at the time.

"Tell me, are you willing to do whatever it takes to get that picture back?"

"Yes. I will do whatever it takes."

"Then the first step is to let go of the picture."

"What? Let go? But that picture is what I want!" I protested.

"Exactly. Let it go."

"But why?" I felt distraught because I did not want to let go of Sonnie.

"We must let go of the pictures, the illusions. That is a picture of what you want, but it may not be what your Higher Power wants for you. The old picture you see is one created from the past. You must let go of the past and be willing to accept whatever is best for your Highest Good."

The drugs started to work. I found it difficult to keep focused. Vida spoke clearly. "Sonnie has made her choice. You must let her go. You cannot control her, or in any way force her to change her mind. The more you resist, the harder it will be for you, not her, but for you.

"By letting go, you are essentially saying, 'This, or something better.' Thus you are releasing your power and allowing your Higher Power to do whatever is in your best long-term interest."

"So, if I want the marriage to work, I must first let it go?"

"That's correct. Let it go," Vida urged.

"But what if Sonnie decides not to come back. Suppose she meets someone else and falls in love with him. Then what?"

"Let her go. Let the marriage go. If it was meant to be, she will return. If not, then accept what is so and move on." He gestured.

"Move on?"

"To this, or, something better!" He smiled. His face was gleaming.

"What could be better?" I was sarcastic.

"You will see. Patience. Patience, love and forgiveness, first. Remember, you are going down your path of Truth. Don't settle for less than the very best the Universe has in store for you. If Sonnie is not willing to work things out, then let it be so. You work your issues and leave her to hers.

"The Father of Light desires to give you the best there is. This, or something better. You'll see. There is something better for you." He touched me on the shoulder, stood and was gone.

The medication took effect. I was drowsy.

There was a knock on the door. "Just checking. How are you feeling?" It was one of the nurses.

"Sleepy. I think I'm going to sleep." I said as I removed my shoes and laid down on the bed. I fell asleep immediately and started dreaming.

— *Fourteen* —

I DREAMT I WAS SLEEPING WITH SONNIE. WE WERE MAKING LOVE, AND I was kissing her face. Gradually I moved to her neck and ear and then to her breast, passionately kissing her soft skin. We were in an old house, one of my childhood homes, built during the reconstruction period in the South. The house had thirteen-foot ceilings, four bedrooms on the second floor, each with its own bathroom. Sonnie and I were in the bedroom my brother and I shared, but he wasn't in the dream.

After we finished making love, I got onto the hardwood floor and attempted to do push-ups, but my strength was gone. I had no power. I then walked over to the bathroom to urinate, but there was no toilet or any other receptacle for me to use. While the room I was standing in was where the bathroom was supposed to be, its furnishings were that of a regular room, such as a den or living room.

Upon awakening, I wrote the dream in my notebook. I wanted to know what, if anything, it meant. That's when I heard Vida's voice.

"Good morning, Eric."

"Hey, Vida. I'm glad you're here. I had a dream about Sonnie and me, and I'm wondering what the interpretation is. Can you help?"

"I can." He took a seat on the other bed.

I read him the dream as I had written it in my notebook. "What do you think?"

Vida sat there for a moment, rubbed his chin, and then he spoke. "Kissing and sucking the breast can symbolize a Higher Power. The infant receives its nourishment from its mother's breast, the then-Higher Power for the infant. In this case, it's not your mother, but Sonnie who has become your Higher Power. You are looking to her for your strength."

"What do you mean?"

"Push-ups are easy for you. As strong as you are, you can do a lot of them, so the fact that you have no power to do push-ups in your dream is significant. You looked to Sonnie for strength, but instead of receiving any, you felt drained."

"You mean, I'm looking to Sonnie to give me strength she can't give?"

"Nor should she, or anyone else for that matter. Your wife is not supposed to be your Higher Power. She should be your friend, partner, lover, but never the source of your power."

"I wasn't aware I looked to her for my power."

"These are old patterns and worn out beliefs that must be changed. The urination scene symbolized that. You tried to urinate, but when you went into the bathroom, there was nowhere for you to go; in fact, the furnishings were inappropriate for a bathroom. You need to eliminate something in your life, but you do not have the appropriate facility to do so. Houses in dreams represent our life structure, or our framework for life. Dreams about old houses that we grew up in signify we are using old ways to structure our lives. You need to examine these old, outdated beliefs."

"Such as?" I swung my legs to the side of the bed.

"Your definition of a wife and a higher power. The old house no longer serves its purpose."

"So, in essence, I have made Sonnie my Higher Power and I have looked to her for inner strength. I need to eliminate that notion from my job description for a wife."

"Correct."

"I also need to find a new Higher Power."

"Correct again."

"Wow! That's really cool!" I felt proud that I got it so quickly.

"There may be an additional interpretation." He crossed his legs.

"Huh?" My pride was short lived.

"The dream presents a karmic possibility."

"What did you mean?"

"Karma is the law of cause and effect. It's the old principle of what you sow, so shall you reap. Karma is the Great Balancer of life. It gives us opportunities to learn through the completion of cycles. In this case, you and Sonnie may have had a relationship from a past life that was left unfinished. You chose this lifetime to complete that which was incomplete. You now have the opportunity to work the karma, or complete the relationship."

"But how do I do that if she doesn't want to work through the marriage?" I was confused, as usual.

"She may be choosing not to complete the cycle. You cannot change her choice. You can change how you respond, from a place of fear to one of Love. By releasing Sonnie and blessing her to her highest good, you complete your part of the karma. Of course, you must do so with a pure heart. Merely saying it is not enough. You must do it with Love for her, not as your wife, but as another divine creation of your Spirit Father."

"Boy. Right now, I don't feel that way. I'm angry, hurt and sad."

"You can use repetition. Say; 'I bless and release Sonnie to her Highest Good.' over and over again. Even if you aren't sincere now, you can be sincere in your desire to truly mean it. So say it, even if you don't mean it today. Eventually you will mean it from your heart."

One of the nurses knocked at my door. "I saw the light on, so I just wanted to check and see if everything is all right."

"Just fine, I'm writing down a dream I had," I replied as I grabbed my pen and paper.

"No problem, just checking." She turned around and left. The ICU wing was sometimes like prison. Every fifteen minutes someone checked up on me.

Vida left the room too. I thought about what he said to me about my dream. It all seemed to fit. I had looked to Sonnie as my Higher Power. I wanted her to validate who I was. Rather than face difficulties head-on, I lost myself in a allegiance to her. As my Higher Power, I tolerated her angry words, her outbursts of swearing and put downs which had become internalized in me. Piece by piece, her hammer of anger had chipped away at what little self-esteem I had. Ironically, I gave her my permission to do it.

Despite that, I still loved Sonnie, perhaps for all the wrong reasons. I may have been unhealthy, and I may have rushed into marriage too soon, but I loved her, as much as I was capable of loving someone.

"Mr. Crane?" It was Dr. Smithson.

"Oh, good morning, doctor." I placed the paper and pen to the side.

"Can we talk for a few minutes?" he asked in a kind tone.

"Sure, your place or mine?" I chuckled, so did he.

We walked out into the common area and found an empty interview room. Inside Dr. Smithson took his usual place behind the desk. I sat across from him.

"So, you had a good night's rest?" He opened up the file as he spoke, then he looked at me.

"Yes sir, I did. Best sleep since I've been in here. What was the medicine you gave me?"

"A combination of tranquilizers and sleep medicine. Under the circumstances you needed to rest, a lot." He smiled. "Tell me what's going on. Are you still thinking about suicide?"

Was I? Vida's words flashed before me. I realized suicide held no answer for me, that it would make matters worse. Faint though it was, a ray of hope existed in my once despondent heart.

"Yes, I've thought about it and I realize it's no longer an option. Perhaps I said those words to Lee out of desperation, who knows. The fact is, I know suicide won't fix my marriage, or me, for that matter.

"This morning I see my situation in a different light. I figure that I have to work this problem with Sonnie out. Maybe she will change her mind, maybe she won't. I can't change the way she thinks, but I can do something about me, and now, I want to stop hurting. I want to stop the war in my head and the pain in my heart."

"Can you share with me how you gained this insight?"

"I'm coming to see I married Sonnie too soon after my divorce from Michele and my break up from Donna. I also realize that my attraction to Sonnie was primarily physical. I suppose I was in no emotional condition to marry her when I did."

"Let's see," Dr. Smithson flipped back through the file. "You got divorced from your first wife in August of '89, then moved in with Sonnie later that year, and married her in April of '90. I'd tend to agree with you, Mr. Crane."

I thought about how absurd it sounded.

"And now that she wants a divorce, what are some of your thoughts?"

"I have angry thoughts. I want to grab her and shake her and make her come around." I felt mad.

"Make her? What would that accomplish?"

"I don't know. On one hand, I love her, and on the other, I hate her. I'm pissed-off, confused, and I hurt. I guess that's why I thought about suicide. I figured 'Why even try any longer?' I've been breaking my back trying to provide a comfortable life for her, and this is the thanks I get." I changed positions in my chair. "So I'm really hoping, Doc, that you can help me." My expression matched my words of sincerity.

Dr. Smithson paused. He cleared his throat and adjusted his necktie, then he put down his pen and said, "I appreciate the profundity of what you just said, Mr. Crane. Your medical condition is treatable, and your emotional state will improve. I am going to put you back in your wing and set up another session with Ms. Sanchez this afternoon." He sat back in his chair and made a note in my file.

"That sounds good. I'd like to get back over there and see my friends," I remarked as he wrote.

"Fair enough, Mr. Crane. I think it would be good for you to see your friends. What about your family? Is there anyone close by who could come and visit you?" He closed the file as he asked.

"My older sister lives here. I could call her. I'm sure she would come." Carla would come at a moment's notice. Being the oldest child in our family, she played the role of my surrogate mother.

"Then I suggest you give her a call and see if she can come visit today or tonight." Dr. Smithson stood up and put his pen in his pocket.

"Okay. I'll do that. Thanks Dr. Smithson." We shook hands, and he walked me back to the room.

"I'll see you again tomorrow," he said as he turned and walked over to the nurses' station to write the transfer orders. I was going back to room 202.

– *Fifteen* –

CARLA WASTED NO TIME IN COMING OVER. I SAW HER IMMEDIATELY AFTER my afternoon session with Lee Sanchez. I received permission to go for a walk with her.

"She's no good for you, Eric. All she ever wanted was a man to take care of her. You're better off without her." Carla was never one to hide her thoughts. Whether you asked her opinion or not, you got it. And, in some matters, she was right.

"It's not that simple," I pleaded. "I love her. I want to work through this, not walk away from it."

"But don't you see, she doesn't want to, so there's no way you can work through it. You need to let her go and start a new life," she implored.

"Right. Just like that. Let her go, and then what. Where do I go? How do I pick up the pieces and start over? It sounds easy, but — I don't know. I'm confused." My heart ached at the thought of giving up Sonnie.

"Don't worry about it now. Your family is behind you on this one. When you get out of here, you can come stay with us until you get your feet back on the ground."

"Thanks. In my head I know you're right about letting her go. Everyone here agrees. I just wish it was that clear to me. Oh well, I guess time will tell, huh?" I was reluctant to have my heart accept what my head was beginning to believe.

"Yep, and she will get what she's got coming to her. You just take care of you. Everything's going to be okay. You'll see."

We had walked halfway around the facility and had some time before we had to return to my wing, so I told her about Abliel and Vida. She listened intently. She believed in angels and spirit guides and accepted my unusual story.

"You know, Eric. Things are going to turn out better than you can imagine. You can't be led like this and have it any other way. In a sense, you are fortunate, and I want you to know that I love you very much."

While she was speaking we had faced one another. When she finished, she took a step toward me and held out her arms. We embraced and as we did, I heard her sniffle. My heart became warm as I too had a tear or two in my eyes.

"Thanks, Carla. That means the world to me."

We said good-bye outside the lobby, and I went back to my wing and thanked Andy for the free time. I had missed the afternoon group because of my session with Lee Sanchez, and Carla's visit. As it was close to dinnertime, I went back to room 202, laid down on the bed and shut my eyes.

"Where do I go from here?" I asked myself silently.

"Wherever you want," was the reply. It was Abliel. "Eric, you must love every person. No matter what. You are loved more than you know. There is no judgment from your Creator. Likewise, you must not judge. You must love. Love is supreme. Love always wins."

"But Abliel, I'm so angry at her for wanting a divorce. How can I love her when all I want to do is strangle her?"

"Loving does not mean you deny your feelings. You have been created with emotions. Feel them. Listen to them. Learn from them. You do not have to hide your emotions for Love to work.

"Love yourself. Love others. Love your Higher Power. But do not judge, for you are not judged. Be angry, but learn from your anger. Let the anger show you where you need to focus your energy to love even more." Abliel always spoke in the same tone, deliberate and slow. He chose each word carefully.

"How do I listen to my anger?"

"Be still. Feel your anger. Ask it what message it has for you. Listen. Learn. Love. That is all for now."

I rolled over on the bed and looked at my watch. Since I still had about twenty minutes before dinner, I decided to give it a try. I faced the wall, my back toward the door. I thought about how much I loved Sonnie how I hated her for wanting to give up on our marriage and walk away. A feeling started to reverberate in my stomach. My thoughts continued and the feeling swelled.

"All right anger. I know you're down there. What do you have to say to me?" I said to myself. My concentration continued on Sonnie. The anger grew. It moved up to my heart, which pounded faster and faster. My stomach churned, my heart pounded and my head was ready to explode. A rush of angry energy gushed up my windpipe and into my mouth. I quickly got up and ran to the toilet, lifted the lid and vomited. The contents of my stomach rushed out with a mighty force in a loud roar, leaving me breathless. I doubled over, barely able to stand, holding on to the wall with one outstretched hand and clutching the sink with the other.

Again, a second wave came up. I gagged and vomited again, forcefully, loudly. I roared like a bear as my body folded at the waist. I was lightheaded.

I must have been real loud because Andy entered the room. "Eric, are you okay? Here let me help." He took a washcloth, wet it, and put it on the back of my neck. I continued to heave, but nothing was left inside. That didn't matter, my anger demon was not finished. It continued to come in torrents and I continued to heave, but by then, there was only air. Andy stood there, holding me. I felt as though I was going to pass out, but I managed to keep standing.

"That's it. Hang in there, dude." Andy offered help in his own way. "All right." He rinsed the washcloth with fresh water and put it back on my neck. "There. Finished?"

I nodded "yes." There was no more to come. Wasted, I stood and stared at the toilet, no energy left to do anything.

"Come on Eric, let's go back to your bed. I'll take care of cleaning up." Andy put his arm around my waist, draped my arm over his shoulders and held my wrist with his hand.

We shuffled over to the bed. Andy turned me around and helped me lay down. By then, another nurse had entered the room.

"What's going on?" she asked as she came over to the bed.

"Eric presented sacrifices at the porcelain alter." Andy replied.

"Cute. Here, let me help." She removed my shoes and socks. Andy had loosened my belt buckle and my trousers.

"We need to change your clothes. You're a mess," said Andy as he continued to get me situated. I nodded as if to say "Okay," but I was too spent to talk.

"Sandy, would you mind looking in the drawer and see what he has to change into? I'm going to get another washcloth to wipe his face." He went back to the bathroom, poured cold water onto a cloth and returned to wipe off my face and hair.

Sandy had opened the drawer that held my clothes. "There's a couple of T-shirts and a pair of jeans here. Maybe he'd like to go to sleep, Andy."

"Eric, do you want to go to sleep?" Andy asked as he continued to wipe me.

"Uh huh," I whispered as I nodded.

"Good idea, Sandy. Let's just give him a clean T-shirt and let him doze." Andy helped me sit up and removed my shirt.

Sandy had come to the side of the bed with my black John Lennon shirt. "Here." She gave Andy the clean shirt and he gave her the dirty one. "I'll start cleaning the bathroom." Her voice trailed behind her as she disappeared into the bathroom.

"Everything under control?" It was Dorothea, the head nurse. She walked into the room. "How you doing, Mr. Eric?"

"Rough, but I'll live." I quietly found a way to make light of the situation.

"Good, we don't want that wife of yours getting any life insurance money now, do we?" Dorothea had her own brand of humor.

"No way." I replied.

"Yeah, you can make me the beneficiary, now," joked Andy. We all laughed.

Sandy came out of the bathroom. "Pretty good aim Eric. I wish my husband was that good."

"Lots of practice." I wasn't kidding, unfortunately.

Dorothea took my vitals. She acted as though everything was okay. "Looks good. How do you feel?"

"Better." I felt wiped out and my body was limp. I could not move a muscle.

"Had you been feeling nauseated?" she asked.

"No, it just kind of came up all of the sudden."

"Hum. Well, just get some rest now. I don't suppose you'll be wanting dinner." Dorothea winked at me and turned around to walk out.

"Yeah, we'll hold it for you." Sandy laughed and walked out with an arm full of towels.

Andy pulled the sheets up. "Take it easy man. I'll be back to check on you later. Get some sleep."

"Thanks, Andy. I'll do just that." He left and I rolled over on my stomach and fell asleep. Before long, I was dreaming again.

I was in the backyard at my house. A shadowy figure appeared in the side yard. It had a feminine appearance. She slowly moved toward me and terror struck my heart as she did. At that moment in my dream I heard Abliel's voice say, "Tell her that the Christ Light within you is greater than the power she has." He repeated it.

I walked slowly toward the dark figure, even though I felt petrified with fear. As I got closer I could see her two red and yellow eyes glowing from within her black hooded cloak. Looking into her demonic eyes, I summoned all the courage I could find and repeated the words Abliel gave me. "The Christ Light in me is greater than the power within you."

At that point, my fear vanished. The figure shrank and moved away from me. I returned to my play in the backyard.

I awoke and searched for my notebook, so that I could record the dream. I though I knew its meaning. I had met a dark being that I thought was more powerful than me. In truth, I had the ultimate power within. Light. Love. It came from my Higher Self, the Christ Light. As I was writing, Vida appeared.

"Hello, Eric." His warm voice was unmistakable.

"Vida. Good to see you." I looked up. "I had a powerful dream and I think I know what it means." With vigor in my voice I recounted the dream and my interpretation.

"Very good." Vida was pleased. "Do you recall our conversation about giving Sonnie power?" He took his place on the other bed.

I nodded as I sat up in my bed.

"Now you see that you do have ultimate power. It comes from the True Center, the Christ Light, your Highest Self. You have the power within to overcome anything; alcoholism, depression, what's going on between you and Sonnie, anything. Do you believe that?"

"I believe that my subconscious believes it, so yes, I suppose I do believe it." Simply by voicing those words, I felt a sense of power and confidence. It gave me strength and hope. I knew that if I stayed in my True Center, I could triumph over life's seemingly difficult obstacles.

"You are learning quickly. Soon you will not need me as much. You will have all you need to go through what you must go through. You must cooperate with your doctor and keep yourself focused upon your True Center. Nothing will have power to conquer you. Life will appear less difficult, and you will begin to experience joy." He smiled.

"You mean, like it says in The Promises?" I said, believing it was so.

"Yes, that's exactly what I mean. You will meet another human who will guide you. He has been through what you must now go through." Vida stood.

"Who is he?"

"It will be revealed soon. For now, be where you are, here in this place. All will come in Divine Time." Vida walked toward me, placed his hand on my shoulder, and vanished.

"Evening meditation, everyone please come to evening meditation," the announcement sounded over the intercom. I had not noticed the time. I remembered it was dinnertime when I had the vomiting spell, so perhaps I slept for a couple of hours, because the evening meditation began at nine o'clock.

I laid down my pen and notebook and walked down the corridor to the open area at the nurses' station. I found a seat by the far wall, next to Kurt.

"Hey, Eric, how are you feeling, man?" Kurt asked.

"A lot better, thanks."

When everyone had gathered, Andy made a few announcements about the next day's schedule, then he turned the gathering over to Pamela, one of the patients.

"Tonight's topic is acceptance. The Big Book of Alcoholics Anonymous says:

"And acceptance is the answer to all my problems today. When I am disturbed, it is because I find some person, place, thing, or situation—some fact of my life—unacceptable to me, and I can find no serenity until I accept that person, place, thing, or situation as being exactly the way it is

supposed to be at this moment. Nothing, absolutely nothing happens in God's world by mistake.

"I need to concentrate not so much on what needs to be changed in the world as on what needs to be changed in me and in my attitudes."

That night's reading had a profound impact on me. In my head, something clicked. Everything was beginning to come together, the dreams, Abliel's counsel, Vida's words, what I had been learning in treatment, it had become apparent to me that I needed to change. My thinking was obviously flawed. It needed to be overhauled, and I was in a place to get the tools I needed to do the job.

We stood in a circle, arms draped over the persons' shoulder who stood on either side, said the Lord's Prayer, and dispersed for the evening.

I went directly to my room. Small tears of gratitude formed in my eyes as I considered Carla's words about how fortunate I was. I turned out the light and got into my bed. A hunch that something dreadful was going to happen found its way into my mind. I tried to ignore it, but it would not go away. I was tired, I decided to go to sleep. It would have to wait until tomorrow.

– *Sixteen* –

THE DARK HUNCH THAT SOMETHING WAS ABOUT TO HAPPEN GREW INTO a larger awareness. For the next three days it grew from a small feeling to a full sense of dread. I was in morning group when one of the staff members opened the door and signaled for me to come outside. This practice was common whenever someone's doctor came for a visit, so I didn't give it much thought, until I was told that Lee Sanchez wanted to see me.

The staffer walked me to Lee's office and told me to have a seat in the waiting area. A look at my watch told me it was ten-forty-three. I wondered what was up. My hunch was taking center stage in my mind. I thought the worst. Perhaps one of the children was seriously ill or injured, or, maybe it was another family member.

I saw some magazines on the table next to me. Nervously I picked one up and flipped through the pages, not stopping to read anything in particular. After a couple of minutes I picked up the second magazine, then the third, the fourth. By then it was five minutes past eleven. My breath came in gasps and I feared an anxiety attack. I told myself that the power in me was greater than the power of whatever was behind Lee Sanchez's door.

Her door opened and Lee appeared. She saw me and a heavy look crossed her face. "Mr. Crane, sorry to keep you waiting. Please come in." I knew something was up because she did not normally call me Mr. Crane, and her smile was forced.

I put down the magazine, stood up and walked into her office. I was surprised to see Dr. Smithson standing there waiting. His presence explained the wait. Usually a true poker face, Dr. Smithson looked serious. His face appeared rigid, his energy subdued.

What would warrant Dr. Smithson and Lee being in the same room to speak to me? I was not too eager to find out. "Dr. Smithson, what brings you here?" I held out my hand to shake his.

"Hello, Mr. Crane. Please, take a seat." He pointed to the sofa as he looked away. Brief eye contact. Lee had closed the door behind me and walked to one of the wing backed chairs across from me. As she sat down she nervously adjusted her skirt. She spoke first. "Mr. Crane, about an hour ago the hospital got some news." She paused and looked over to Dr. Smithson. "Given the circumstances, I thought it best if Dr. Smithson was here too. I hope you don't mind."

"No, uh, that's okay. What is it?" My anxiety was now a dismal, dire feeling. Dr. Smithson uncrossed his legs and leaned forward in his chair.

"Sonnie, was in a car accident earlier this morning." His face was stone somber.

"Oh no!" My words came out in hushed astonishment.

"She was rushed to the hospital where they did everything they could, but," he cleared his throat, "she passed away in the operating room. I'm so sorry, Eric." Dr. Smithson's voice had quivered. That was the first time he had called me Eric.

I stared at the carpet, institutional gray. Perfect for thinking about nothing while you're waiting for your heart to start beating again. I had a premonition, but never, never had anything like Sonnie's death entered my head. "Did he say Sonnie was dead? He did. Maybe he didn't mean it. Of course he did." A dialog broke out in my head as ice cold shock froze my mouth.

"Mr. Crane, are you okay?" Dr. Smithson interrupted my thoughts.

"Humph. Well, that depends on what you mean by okay, Doc." I said sullenly.

"This is a delicate matter. I am wondering what your thoughts and feelings are." He replied.

"Feelings? What should I feel? I don't know, I - oh Jesus," I felt a flash flood of emotion in the pit of my stomach and the back of my head that I fought long enough to ask, "What happened?"

"We don't know the specifics." Lee spoke in a very soft, caring manner. "She was involved in a multi-car wreck and wasn't wearing a seat belt. She was thrown from the car and flown to Memorial Hospital. That's all we know."

"What about my children, where are they?" I asked worriedly.

"Sonnie's father called your sister in law. She will get them from school this afternoon. I have spoken to Carla. She's on her way here to see you."

"Mr. Crane, I am going to allow you a temporary discharge, so you can take care of matters, but I want to wait a couple of hours before you leave while I look in to a few things. Okay?" Dr. Smithson looked at the file and then back to me.

I nodded "okay" in a mechanical manner. Tears were coming up. I looked around. Sensing what I was looking for, Lee Sanchez reached over to her desk, picked up a box of pink tissues and handed them to me. I took one and wiped my nose.

"How are you sleeping, Mr. Crane?" asked Dr. Smithson.

"Pretty good, I guess." I shrugged.

"I'm going to give you prescriptions that I want you to follow exactly as indicated. I want to hear from you every day."

"Sure. Fine." I spoke quietly. Everything felt unreal.

"Is there anything else we can do?" Lee asked as she leaned forward.

"Not now. Well, maybe. I'd like to call my office."

"No problem. You can use the phone here on my desk. I'll show you. Anything else?" Lee's expression showed genuine compassion.

"No, that will do. I just need some time to think about things."

"That's fine. After you're done with the phone call, we'll walk you back to your room. You can rest there." Dr. Smithson said as he stood up.

Lee stood and so did I. She showed me the telephone. "Just punch a line and then dial nine to get an outside line."

"Thanks." My tone was solemn. I dialed the office number. It rang four times before Carrie answered. "Hi, Carrie, it's Eric."

"Eric, how are you feeling?"

"Better. I'm doing better." I attempted to fake how I felt.

"You don't sound better. Are you okay?"

I endeavored to sound normal. "Yeah, is Frank in?"

"Sure, he's on the phone. I'll let him know you're waiting."

"Thanks." I wiped my nose with the tissue.

"You're welcome. Please, hold on." After a few seconds she came back. "Okay Eric, he's going to take your call. Here you go."

"Thanks, Carrie."

"Eric? Is that you?" Frank was enthusiastic.

"Hi. Yeah, it's me." My voice was low.

"Well, how are things going? You sound down."

"That's why I'm calling. Frank, uh, Sonnie has been in a car wreck, and - ah damn it, Frank, she's dead!" I broke down.

"Oh, Eric." Frank's tone went from enthusiastic to disbelief.

I tried to get my composure back. "I gotta go Frank."

"I'll be right over. We'll get through this. I'll be there soon."

That was reassuring. "Thanks. Carla's on her way though."

"Good. I still want to come, if that's okay with you?"

"Okay, talk to you later." I hung up the phone and said a little "thank-you" to the heavens. It felt good to hear Frank's voice and to know he was on his way. I stood and Lee Sanchez was standing close by.

"I thought you might want these." She handed me the box of tissues.

"Thanks." I took two.

"I'll go with you back to your room," said Lee. We walked together down the corridor to the wing, without conversation. I held the box of tissues and kept my eyes focused on the three feet or so of the floor in front of me. We turned the corner and entered the doors to my wing.

"Here we are. I'll let you know when Carla gets here," Lee uttered as she stopped.

"Okay. Thanks, Lee."

"You're quite welcome. Things will work out. You're in good hands with Dr. Smithson. See you later." She held out her hands and offered me a hug.

I went into room 202. Lee remained at the nurses' station to talk. I assumed she was letting them know what was going on.

I laid on my bed, picked up my notebook and opened it to a clean page and started to write. *"Today I got nuked. Sonnie is dead. This open stuff sucks. It hurts too damn much. I think I'll go back to being closed."*

I heard a knock on the door. It was Andy.

"I just heard, man."

"Hi, come in." I spoke with little emotion.

Andy brought in a tray of food. "I thought I'd bring lunch to you, in case you were hungry." He sat the tray on the desk.

"Thanks a lot." I had no appetite, but appreciated his thoughtfulness.

"Lee filled us in. Wow, this one is tough." Andy moved over to the other bed.

"Really, I don't know, man. It's all happened so fast. I'm kind of in shock mode." I looked out the window.

"Well, you're in a safe place. If you've got to fall apart, this is the place to do it."

"That's exactly how I feel, like I'm going to fall apart. My world has crashed, and there's nothing I can do! I'm going to loose it!" I turned away from the window and put my face in my hands.

Andy came over and put his hand on my back. "That's right, man, go ahead, cry. It's okay, cry all you want."

I sobbed. After all the emotional turmoil of the past several days, I figured I was cried-out. I was wrong. That cry emanated from an unknown cavern. Andy found the box of pink tissues and handed them to me. I went through them quickly. There wasn't much to say. It wasn't a time for words. It was a time for feeling, a time to let it out. Andy was right, the Institute was a safe place. There was no booze, and I could cry, shout, go nuts, anything, because after all, I was already in the booby hatch.

Andy's name was called over the intercom.

"I'll be back in a minute. Don't stop. It's okay. Don't stop." He left the room and headed down the corridor toward the nurses station.

I laid face first into my pillow. I sobbed and wailed. I felt hurt way down in the most remote recess of my being, and it needed to come out. It did. I let it. And it was okay.

I felt a hand on my back, softly stroking me like my grandmother had done when I was a child. I looked up and no one was there. I must have imagined it. I turned back to bury my face in my pillow and noticed it again. I felt it. It was real. Again, no one was there. "You must really be losing it, Crane," I thought.

Turning back toward the pillow, I buried my face again and kept crying. That time I sensed the presence of someone in the room. "Andy's back," I thought. I looked up and no one was there. "This is weird. What's going on? Where's Abliel?" I wondered.

"I'm here, Eric." Abliel's voice soothed me.

"Was that you touching me?"

"No. It was not me," he gently replied.

"Then who? Vida?"

"No. It's Bernice." Bernice is my late grandmother.

"Granny?" I marveled.

"Yes. Granny," he answered.

"She's here?"

"Right here, and has been since you collapsed at home."

"Why didn't you tell me?"

"It wasn't time."

"Can I see her? Speak to her?" I direly wanted to.

"You can speak to her the same way you speak to me."

I was apprehensive, but thought "Hey, you're talking to your Guardian Angel, a Spirit Guide, your Self, why not Granny! After all, remember where you are!" I thought I'd give it a try. "Granny?" I asked timidly.

"Hi, Eric, honey." It was her voice I heard in my mind.

"Granny, is that really you?"

"Yes indeed." She always said that.

"Oh Granny," I continued crying. Her hand rubbed my back. "It hurts so much. I don't know if I can take it."

"I know. It may seem impossible, but we never get more than we can handle. You have a lot of support on this side. And your Moma is praying for you, and so is Carla." Her voice brought comfort to me.

"I don't know what to say. It's all pretty overwhelming right now. I never thought in a million years that I would be going through something like this at this point in my life."

"We all must go through whatever we need to go through to learn the lessons we choose to learn." Her voice brought comfort.

"But I don't think I would have chosen to learn it this way."

"Oh honey, right now it seems hard to imagine choosing a path with so much pain, but that's where you are right now, and you can go through it. You can make it through this and once you do, you won't have to do it again, ever!" I wanted to believe what she said.

"How long will it last?" I needed to know.

"I can't say. That's up to you. But remember, I am here, as are others. We all hold Light for you, so you can see your way through the darkness. When you feel the pain the most, we will be here for you. Remember that. Remember we love you and hold Light for you. There is no greater power in all the Universe and it's all here for you."

With that my crying stopped. I had a moment of peace, some assurance that I could make it through the lesson that lay ahead. Deep in my center, a small, peaceful feeling slowly spread like the warmth of a glowing fire. Maybe being open was working, because if I had been drinking, I wouldn't have felt like this. I'd have felt hopeless, and then I wouldn't have felt anything, until the next day, when everything would have been compounded with a sick hangover.

"Knock, knock." Andy returned. "Sorry Eric, I had to take a call. Feel better?"

"Much better, thanks." I sat up on the bed.

"I hope you can deal with as much of your feelings as you can while you're here. This is the place to do it. Not that you can get through it all, but at least if you can get some of the stuff out while you're here, you'll be better equipped to deal with it when you get on the outside."

"I hope so, I really do." I gathered up the used tissues and threw them in the trash can.

"See if you can eat. You need to keep your nourishment up. You'll want to get some exercise too."

"Thanks. I appreciate all your help."

"Not at all. I'm just passing on what someone had done for me once."

"Really? Were you ever in here?" I asked.

"Seven years ago," he replied.

"Please, sit down." I motioned him to the other bed. "Tell me about it."

"I was strung out on coke and booze. I had lost everything, job, wife, car, house, you name it. I came in here with nothing. No self respect, nothing. I was broken, beat up and ready to die, but when I got here, someone sort of adopted me and helped me through it."

We talked a while. Andy shared his story with me about how, after treatment, he went back to school for training in substance abuse counseling. Being on the Peachtree Institute staff paid the bills while he continued to work on his MSW. Eventually, he planned to get a Ph.D. in psychology and specialize in addiction counseling. He was committed to seeing his dream through.

"That's an incredible story. So here you are, right here, right now. I was told I would have someone to guide me."

"Told? Who told you?" he asked.

He would really think I had lost it if I explained. Oh well, I thought, what did I have to lose?

"My Spirit Guide." I said. Not knowing what his response would be, so I said it sort of on the timid side.

"You too! I have a Spirit Guide!" He smiled.

"No kidding! Wow! I was afraid you'd think I was crazy! That's amazing!" I was relieved. "You believe in that sort of thing, then?"

"I do. Spirituality is as real to me as the bed you're sitting on. I believe we must heal in the physical, emotional and spiritual bodies, but the first thing is sobriety. Without that, the other bodies can't heal. That's why I do this kind of work. I am the first line of recovery. I provide the base, from there each one works his, or her, own program."

"Much of what I've learned here has had a significant impact on me. The Promises, the Steps, a Higher Power, the idea of acceptance, it all fits together. I don't understand it all yet, but it feels correct." I was having trouble communicating the depth of my experience.

"Take your time. This isn't a race. It's not about who gets to Step Twelve first. This is life. It's a whole new way of living. The program provides the tools. You provide the attitude. We do this one day at a time. We don't try to get it all at once. You take what fits for today, and leave the rest for later. Today is all we have."

I thought about what Vida had said about being in the moment.

"You're doing so well with this. If you have questions, you can call me at any time, okay?" Andy sounded sincere.

"Okay, thanks." We both stood. I started to offer him my hand, when he held out both arms.

"Hugs are allowed," he said with a smile.

We hugged. Two guys, two alcoholics, two brothers, two kindred souls.

Sandy came to the door. "Eric, there's a Frank Watson here to see you."

"Great. I'm on my way." I quickly ran my hands through my hair. "Okay?" I asked Andy.

"Sure, see you later." He smiled as I left.

Sandy walked me to an interview room where Frank was waiting.

"Hey, Eric." Frank greeted me.

"Hey, Frank." We shook hands.

"How are you doing?" he asked as he sat down.

"I'll make it. The people here are fantastic. I'm getting a lot of support, and Carla's on her way to take me to…" I hesitated, "to be with Sonnie." I sat in the usual patient's chair.

"Well, listen, I don't want to take up a lot of your time, but I do want you to know that everything is okay at the office. You take all the time you need to get through this."

"That's good news. I appreciate it, a lot. I don't know how much time that will be."

"That's fine. If it takes a few more weeks, then that's what it takes. You're on paid leave, so take it, whatever it takes, okay?" His serious look turned into a smile.

"Frank, that's very generous of you. How can I ever thank you enough?"

"Get better. Get through this and take care of yourself and your children. Work will always be there, but your family comes first."

"You're right. I know that now. I guess it's too late, though." I looked down and choked up.

"It's never too late. You still have a whole life in front of you. Take this time-out to get yourself together for the second half." Frank liked to speak in sports terminology.

"Yeah, right. The second half. It feels more like the final seconds of the fourth quarter, Frank and I'm down by a couple of touchdowns."

"That's not true. You just fumbled the ball. Regroup. You'll land on your feet. One bad game doesn't ruin the whole season. You'll come back stronger than before. Just don't give up. Never, ever give up."

"Sure. I won't." I remarked quietly.

There was a knock at the door.

"Yes?" I answered.

Andy opened it. "Excuse me, but Carla's waiting in Lee Sanchez's office."

"Okay." I could not wait to see her so I immediately stood.

"We're finished," Frank said to Andy.

We shook hands. Frank grabbed my elbow with his other hand. That's a business man's hug.

"You'll make it, Eric. Hang in there," he said.

"Thanks. I'll see you later, huh?"

"You bet." He walked out of the room and down the corridor.

 Andy asked, "Is everything all right?"

"Yeah, fine. Let's go."

— *Seventeen* —

SEEING THE HUMAN BODY WITHOUT ITS LIFE IS LIKE LOOKING AT A stone. It vaguely resembles the person you knew, more like a mannequin or a wax statue than a human being. If ever I had a doubt about whether or not there is more to life than what exists on the earth plane, standing next to Sonnie's corpse erased it. As I looked at her, I knew that there was no more "Sonnie." What remained was a lifeless form, devoid of any sense of personality. I touched her hand. Cold. No sensation. Just cold, hard, lifeless flesh.

A few days earlier, in Lee Sanchez's office, Sonnie was telling me the marriage wasn't working. At that moment, I felt as though a javelin had been thrust into my heart. Standing next to her in the morgue, I felt as though someone had turned that javelin, first to the right, then to the left and finally thrust it forward once more before withdrawing it, along with my insides. Sonnie was gone. I wanted a drink. Correction. I wanted a million drinks.

So many feelings swirled around inside me that I couldn't feel. So many words danced in my mouth that I couldn't speak. So many thoughts raced in my mind that I was unable to think clearly.

I fought to find some balance, some point where I could focus. I searched the alcoves of my mind for an answer, a reason, a purpose. One word found its way out of the pack of words and thoughts. Like a sperm that finally reaches the egg, one word valiantly struggled victoriously to the surface of my mind. "Why?"

Then another word, "now?"

And finally, "me?"

Carla was with me. Silently and patiently, she waited those minutes while I stood frozen next to Sonnie's body. She stepped closer, touched my arm and took my left hand in hers, saying nothing. She sniffled and wiped her nose with a tissue.

Outside the door stood a man from the funeral home, dressed in a funeral home suit and a funeral home haircut. Perfect. Conservative, but perfect. No smile, only a solemn look. Carla had spoken to him before she joined me. She was making the logistical arrangements.

"It's time Eric. They need to take her, now." She whispered softly.

"Okay." I sniffled, took one last look at Sonnie, and I thought I heard her answer, "Because."

Carla walked with me out of the morgue, through the hospital to the parking lot. It was dusk, the sun had set behind thin pink and orange clouds. The wind blew my hair into my eyes. I stood numbly while Carla unlocked the doors. Our children were born in this hospital, and Sonnie had died here. I got into the car, put on my seat belt and looked straight ahead. "Where can I get a drink?" I thought. "Forget it, Crane, that won't bring her back." I had a battle going on in my mind. "Yeah, but at least it won't hurt as bad if I'm drunk." "Right. Like it won't be there tomorrow, hurting worse, because then you'll be hungover. Besides, what about the kids? Who's going to take care of them?" A battle with a bottle can't be won. It's best not to start it. "Stinking thinking" they call it in recovery.

"Let's go." I blurted out, signaling to my mind that the battle was over, for that moment.

I had not seen the children. Will was only two and a half. He would never understand I thought. Amy was barely four. What would I say? How could I explain to them that their Mommy wasn't coming back home? I had to think fast; Carla's house was only a few minutes away, and they were waiting there for me.

"What have you told them?" I needed Carla's input.

"That Mommy was in an accident, and you were coming home to be with them."

"Oh." I looked straight ahead.

"How do you want to do this?" she asked as she pulled out of the parking lot.

"I don't know. What do you think?"

"That's a tough one. Just be honest. I'm sure the right words will come somehow." We stopped for a traffic light. "Tell them Sonnie was in an accident, and she was hurt so bad that she died."

It sounded too easy. She died. This morning she got them dressed; now she's dead; I'll get them undressed.

We drove for what seemed like a few seconds. I dreaded going into the house. I had not seen them in a couple of weeks, and this was not the homecoming I had intended. As we turned in to Carla's street, my heart began thumping as sweat beaded on my forehead and above my top lip. Another drink thought flashed across my mind. "Forget it. Not now. Not for the next hour, anyway." I put the thought of drinking on a sixty-minute hold.

The car pulled up the driveway, the garage door opened, and I wished time would stop, but the car was the only thing that did. As I walked through the garage door into the kitchen, I heard two little voices squeal in excitement.

"Daddy, Daddy, Daddy!" They came running at full speed and did not stop until they both ran into a leg. I squatted to get to hugging height.

"Hi, Will; hi, Amy, umm, it's so good to see you." We embraced.

"We missed you, Daddy!" Amy exclaimed.

"Miss you, Daddy." Will echoed.

"Where's Mommy?" Amy asked as she looked behind me.

"Mommy," echoed Will.

"She's not here, love. Come on, let's go in the other room."

"Okay." Amy grabbed my hand as I stood up.

"Kay." Will took the other hand.

We walked into the living room. I sat on the couch and put Amy on one leg and Will on the other.

"I need to tell you something." I cleared my throat. "Mommy was in a bad car wreck today."

"Car wreck?" asked Will.

"Yes, that's right. You know when two cars go BOOM!" I took my fists and butted them together.

"Is she okay? Is Mommy hurt?" Amy looked worried.

"Yes, Mommy was hurt." Now for the big one. "She's not coming home. She's … " I took a deep breath, reached for courage and continued. "Well, Mommy was hurt so bad that she, uh, she, died." I started to lose it.

"Whasth 'died', Daddy?" Will asked.

"Oh no! Not Mommy!" Amy understood.

I wiped my eyes. "Died means, like when you step on an ant, the ant dies." Surely I could do better than that. "You remember the Lion King?"

"Uh huh." Will shook his head affirmatively.

"Well, remember when Mufasa died?"

"Scar was mean and he killed him!" Amy explained.

"That's right. Well, Mommy was killed when the two cars hit each other."

"Car mean?" Will asked.

"Yes, uh, no, son, the car was not mean. But when the cars go BOOM, it hurts people and Mommy got hurt so bad that she was killed."

"But I want Mommy!" Amy started crying.

"Want Mommy!" Will started, too.

"Me too," I said. "Me too." I pulled them closer. We hugged and wept. Sonnie was gone, and we hurt. We ached. In bitterness and sadness, we sat together and felt the greatest pain of all. Death. The amazing part is that I no longer needed a drink.

– *Eighteen* –

THE LED DISPLAY ON MY CLOCK-RADIO SAID THREE-TWELVE. THE trouble was that it was A.M. I was wide awake, unable to turn off the chatter in my head. I had brought Amy and Will home after dinner at Carla's. Getting them to bed was no easy chore, for children have thoughts and feelings too.

We read a couple of stories and said a prayer. I let them drink two cups of water, cleaned out the monsters from under their beds and said good-night to all their stuffed animals. By ten o'clock they were finally asleep.

I wandered through the house, remembering the past three years. In the corner of the living room by the stereo, Sonnie and I had danced slow dances until early in the morning. In the kitchen, we made meals together while entertaining family for Thanksgiving and Christmas. In the dining room, I had put together Christmas toys while Sonnie arranged all of the stockings and presents under the tree.

Next I went to the bedroom. It started out as our bedroom, then it became hers as I had moved to the guest room. We were two people entangled in a messed-up love who could not live happily together.

I walked over to the bed and sat on the side where Sonnie slept. I smelled her pillow. Her scent was still there. I got up and walked into the bathroom, where her makeup still lay on the counter. She was always sure to get it on perfectly, sometimes taking two hours or more. That used to make me angry, but *this* night, it seemed insignificant.

The picture I had taken in Trinidad hung in a brass frame next to the mirror. Sonnie and I had walked on the beach holding hands. As I looked back at our footprints I noticed my feet pointed out to either side, while Sonnie's pointed straight ahead. Mine were large and hers were small. I had marveled then at how we could walk so differently, yet move in the same direction, so I took a picture of it. From now on there would be only one set of footprints in the sand, I thought as I looked away from the picture.

I walked into her closet. In the midst of her clothes, I sensed Sonnie. I had bought most of them; the pink and white cable knit sweater from Nieman-Marcus, the lavender skirt from Rich's, the black evening dress from Macy's, with high heels to match from Parisian. She wore that outfit in Palm Springs. Each article had a story, a memory of times spent together.

Then I saw the lime green hatbox where she kept pictures and memento's. I didn't want to open it at first, but I quickly changed my mind. Inside were all the cards I had sent to her. Birthdays, anniversaries, child births, cards from when I was in the dog house and cards for no particular reason at all, other than I loved her. Funny, I had not sent any cards in a long while.

She kept photographs, too. Our honeymoon was in Captiva, Florida. We liked the Gulf Coast more than the Atlantic side, because the water was clear and blue, and the beaches had clean, white powdery sand. Sonnie and I had made love in the Gulf water one evening with no one around but the man in the moon.

One photo was taken Christmas Eve three years before. Sonnie's father, her sister and brother-in-law had come over. The turkey took an unusually long time to cook. Eight hours, in fact. We ate dinner at eleven that night before everyone rushed home for Christmas morning.

There were pictures from a mini-trip to the mountains of North Georgia we had taken four years earlier. The leaves were turning, creating a patchwork quilt of orange, sunburst red, green and yellow. We did it in nature that Sunday afternoon. Our romance was at its apex. Amy was at Sonnie's sister's house that day, allowing us an afternoon of love and passion.

The photographs were the legacy of a marriage that started with fireworks and ended with cold ashes. We wanted it all, but couldn't give anything for it. Play now, pay never. Live life to its fullest with booze, sex and credit cards.

I shut the box and walked out of the closet, closing the door as I left, leaving the memories in her hatbox.

Back in the bedroom, I decided to sleep in "our" bed. I undressed and slipped in between the sheets. Sonnie wasn't there, so I took a couple of pillows and held them like I had held her in nights past. It was half past midnight. I lay awake, looking out the window into the night. It was dark, with only a sliver of the moon visible. The night creatures sang in the woods, and I listened with tears welling up in my eyes.

"Oh Sonnie, why now? Why this time? Why wasn't it working for you? What did I do that was so awful? Was it really that bad?" The thoughts came like a snow blizzard, blinding my ability to see the truth. The truth that said the marriage had died long before.

I reached over to the night table for a tissue to wipe my nose. "No, no, no!" I shouted, into the pillow. Fearing I would wake up the children, I got up to close the door. I grabbed a dirty T-shirt because by then the tissues weren't cutting it.

Back in the bed, an energy from within convulsed my body into the fetal position. I ached. Deep, ancient hurt came out with a powerful force behind it. It continued for an hour or so, like a hurricane, with no signs of relenting. Dark feelings, dark energy, came seemingly from nowhere. How could I have so many tears? Surely there was an end point.

Finally, at about two in the morning, it stopped. Exhausted, I lay there looking at the wall. My contact lenses felt like sand paper, so I got up and took them out. I put on my glasses and went back to the bed. I had no energy left, but I couldn't sleep, couldn't rest.

"Want to talk about it?"

Vida was in the room.

"I'm too tired to talk tonight. I just want to go to sleep and wake up with Sonnie here in my arms like the old days."

"Ah, the old days. Yes. Who doesn't want the old days? They were fun, carefree, full of romance and love. Not like recent days, full of arguments and fights, bills and money problems, stress and…."

"Not now Vida, please, I want to remember the good things. Can't I just do that?" I sat up on the side of the bed.

"Sonnie is gone. You can't bring her back. The memories will always be with you, but you can't stay there, in the past, you have to be here, in the present."

"Why? Why can't I be back there?" I argued.

"Because. God is here, now; not there, then; but right here. Life is about what's going on now. You can remember the past; that's okay, but you must live life in the here and now, put your energy in the present and accept things as they are."

I didn't want to hear what he had to say. I wanted to reminisce about the days when Sonnie and I were in love.

Vida was still speaking. "You can't undo the past. Sonnie is gone from this earth plane, and that will not change. You can influence your present with our thoughts and actions. Living in the past consumes energy required to live in this moment." He leaned against the window and gestured.

"You learned from Sonnie. Find the lessons. Glean your truth from the past, and avoid making the same mistakes. The marriage wasn't working. It hadn't for some time. Now Sonnie has moved on, and you must heal. It takes time."

"Heal? I feel drained, like there's nothing left inside."

"First things first. Rest. Get some sleep. Tomorrow will have its lesson for you. Be prepared." He walked over, put his hand on my head and left.

For a moment, I pondered about what he meant about being prepared. It was no use. I was exhausted, so I laid back down. It was three-twelve, and in a few hours, Will and Amy would awaken. I had to get some sleep.

"God, uh, HP, if you'll allow me to abbreviate Higher Power, right now I need to sleep. I have a busy day tomorrow, well, later today, so please let me sleep. That's all I ask for, sleep." I rolled over, got into my sleeping position and nodded off, alone.

— *Nineteen* —

DICK DUNLOP OFFICIATED AT THE FUNERAL. HE AND I HAD SPENT AN hour together discussing Sonnie's death. Dick had prayed that I might find peace through all of it. One thing he said made an impression upon me.

"When we walk through the Valley of Death, Eric, we fear no evil. I like to spell evil backwards. L-i-v-e. We will not fear to *live*."

Something in my head said "keep that one."

Dick continued. "We find the courage and strength to move forward with our Shepherd leading the way. At this time, it may be difficult for you to hear the Shepherd's voice, but I encourage you to try, for it is always there. Always." He winked and looked at me as if he knew firsthand what he was talking about. We then prayed and walked to the chapel.

My family was already seated. Dad had made arrangements for my children, from my marriage with Michele, to fly in. I had met with them earlier that morning, finding comfort in their presence.

Felicia was only nineteen, but she spoke like a woman much more experienced. "We want you to know that we all love you, Dad. We want to help you get through this." I felt the combined strength of them all as they each expressed their love for me in their own unique way.

I walked down the aisle and took my seat with my children. Carla sat with us too. The organ was playing "Amazing Grace." I sang the words to myself:

"Amazing grace, how sweet the sound,
That saved a soul like me.
I once was lost, but now am found.
Twas blind, but now I see."

I reached into my pocket for a handkerchief. I wiped my eyes and nose. I heard sniffles on either side of me. A quick look, and the children were all crying. I stretched my long arms over as many of them as I could and pulled them closer.

Behind us sat my mom and dad. I could hear Dad trying too choke back his emotions. A child of the Depression, Dad was not one to openly express how he felt. His presence provided much needed strength for me. Although Dad was a quiet man, his love for his children was expressed openly. I was glad to have a close relationship with him.

Mom was different. She cried anywhere and anytime she felt like it, and that day she wept plenty.

I looked to the other side of the aisle. Sonnie's family was there. Her sister was crying, and her father had a handkerchief in his hand. Sonnie's only living grandparent was there. Grandpa was a short man, but physical and spiritual statures were two different things. With an Italian father and a French mother, Grandpa was one feisty man. I loved his direct way of communicating. You never had to guess with him. He wept too.

I don't remember much of what Dick Dunlop said from the pulpit. I do remember Sonnie's spirit was with us. I felt it. I think everyone else did, too. A woman from the church choir sang "People Who Need People." If I ever needed people, it was then. I quietly thanked God for all the people in my life. Each one had his or her own gift in expressing love toward the human race.

After the service, the kids and I rode in a limousine to the graveside. Sonnie's family mentioned cremating her body, but I thought Will and Amy were too young for that. It was important for them to see Sonnie and watch the burial as a ceremony to help bring completion to their relationship with her.

At the grave, we took our seats in front, Will and Amy with me, the other children behind me with their hands on my shoulders. Dick read the Twenty-third Psalm. I reflected on what he told me about having courage to live. That's when I looked across the way to see Andy and some of my new friends from Peachtree Institute standing there. They had come just for me. I was overcome with emotion.

When they lowered Sonnie into the ground, Will and Amy stood up to see it go all the way to the bottom.

"Mommy gone there, Daddy?" Will pointed to the grave as he asked.

"Yes, son, Mommy is going down there." I whispered back.

"Mommy!" Will cried out. "Bye-bye." He waved.

"This is for you, Mommy!" cried Amy as she threw a flower into the grave where the coffin rested.

Dick said a prayer. I looked up and saw Lee Sanchez standing behind him. Dr. Smithson was at the opposite side of the grave. Overhead a jet was flying towards an unknown destination. Birds were singing their songs. People around the grave were crying. I felt the presence of Abliel and Vida and Granny. That gave me a lot of comfort.

After the service, those in attendance came over and offered words of comfort and condolences.

"We love you, Eric.

"We'll miss her, too."

"Come see us when you can."

"Hang in there, man."

"You're not alone. We are all with you."

One by one, they passed by. Some spoke, others merely grabbed an arm and squeezed, saying nothing, but delivering a message of love, nonetheless.

Finally they walked off. I stayed behind for a few moments. I looked around to be sure I was alone, because I wanted to say my farewell in private.

"Good-bye, Sonnie. Maybe it would have worked, maybe not. I hope you find peace. I hope you find whatever it is you were looking for, but couldn't find with me." I started to leave, then turned back and with a throat full of emotion said, "I love you, Wook."

I walked to the limo. The children were inside waiting. No one spoke during the ride back to the funeral home.

I finally broke the silence by clearing my throat. "You kids will never know how much you mean to me right now." My chin quivered. "You mean everything to me." I lost it. They gathered around me, and we held one another for the remainder of the long ride home.

That night, after saying good-night to everyone else, I got undressed and crawled into bed. It was my bed.

"Abliel?"

"Yes, Eric."

"Thanks. Thanks for being there today. Thanks for everything." I looked up at the ceiling.

"You are welcome. There is an abundance of love for you right now. I know you feel it." His words were reassuring.

"Yes, I do feel it."

"Love is the only real power. It will get you through this. Have faith. Don't quit. Keep wanting to live, and live wanting to love."

"Thanks." I was back to that one word. I had made it through the toughest day of my life and I wasn't thinking about getting loaded. I was grateful. I was counting my blessings, and "thanks" was the only word that would do.

My life was about to enter a new phase, one of honesty and God awareness that some call spirituality. I felt as though I was about to step off a cliff, not knowing whether I would fall or fly. My old life patterns had failed and I had to discard them. I had no choice, but to take that next step, into the unknown where I yielded my will to that of my Higher Power. Awaiting me was a life of faith where I no longer directed the show, a life of surprise in each magical moment, a world of splendor where I could find joy in who I was and where I was.

I made a commitment that night to no longer live in fear, but to take the step of faith and be me. To be authentic. To be the creation that my Higher Power created me to be, Eric Crane.

– *Epilogue* –

FOUR YEARS HAVE PASSED SINCE SONNIE DIED. THE EMOTIONAL DEVAS-
tation of the demise of our marriage and her tragic death wreaked havoc
in my gut and my head, and for the first year, I merely survived the loss,
dating no one. Sometime after the initial six months, I noticed that the
crying spells had become less frequent, and I found days with peace and
serenity. By the ninth month, I had only a few difficult days. By the
twelfth month, I had almost none.

I found a therapist who helped me move beyond the legend of
Sonnie. Through many challenging sessions, I waded through the car-
nage of a relationship that had little hope of ever recovering on its
own. I realized that I had surrendered a part of my self to Sonnie's insatiable appetite of what she called "being in love." I had donated my
soul, so that she could be satisfied and fulfilled, so that our marriage
would "work," as she so often phrased it.

Once I got past those issues, I was able to commence the rebuilding
process. I got to a point where I could accept myself for who I was,
and I found that loving myself, unconditionally, was possible. It was a
liberating lesson for which I can now bless Sonnie, who chose to provide me with experiences necessary for my Soul's growth.

About the beginning of year two, I noticed an attractive woman
who intrigued me. Initially, I merely observed her from a distance. She
attended the church that the children and I occasionally visited. Her
shoulder-length blond hair, and her deep blue eyes were beacons of

beauty. Her presence seemed pleasant and familiar. I made no effort to get to know her that year. I knew I wasn't ready for a relationship, and my history was to find someone, fall in love and move in, all in the same week. I knew that I had to wait until I was ready to begin seeing someone new, and I also knew in my next relationship, I would have to do things altogether differently.

I never even knew her name. Too shy to ask, I was content to remain anonymous, a background person hidden in the scenery. She always smiled as she greeted others. I noticed, from some of the functions I attended, she talked to many different people, rather than hanging out with one group all the time. I liked that. She did not smoke; I liked that as well.

As summer turned to autumn and autumn to winter, I began to feel a desire to date. A relationship was out of the question at that point, so I rationalized the woman at church was not a candidate, because I sensed there was more to her than Saturday socializing. I looked at women everywhere, wondering who I might ask out. There are thousands of single women in Atlanta. It is a Southern Mecca for singles. I tried a dating service, but gave up after several months of less than stellar results, because the women turned out to be different than how they had been represented.

Spring emerged with its bright flowery dogwoods and its dazzling, colorful azaleas. The desire to have someone more permanent in my life continued to grow, and like the spring season, my being was experiencing new growth with small telltale signs that I, too, was growing and changing into a more beautiful creature.

I was learning to laugh and play with Will and Amy. I even went so far as to go down the slide at the playground with them! I enjoyed playing their games and listening to them as they talked to me. At night, I read them stories. Among their favorites were the Dr. Seuss collection. As I tucked Will and Amy into bed, I gave each one a kiss and said, "I love you." Later, after they drifted off into their dreams, I walked into their bedroom and stood there. I once thought of how nice it would be if Sonnie and I were standing there together, arm in arm, watching our little angels as they slept. I fantasized about it until I felt lonely and longed for her, then I went into my bedroom and played my mental tape to the end, to the scene where we fought over anything and nothing. To the part where we began our exit scenario. Then I returned to the moment and practiced acceptance of the situation as it was.

The church we attended held a picnic on Memorial Day weekend. I promised Will and Amy I would take them, because it included swimming and other fun activities. We were in the water, playing and splashing about, when I noticed the woman I admired enter the pool area. She walked over to the deep end, pulled up a chaise lounge and laid down to sunbathe.

I continued to play with the kids while sneaking glances over at her. Again, I observed no smoking. Good. She was reading a paperback book, but because of the distance between us, I could not see what it was. She wore sunglasses, so I had to be discreet in my observations; sunglasses allow people to hide their eye movements. After a few hours, we went home. Going home was easier than walking over and introducing myself.

About two weeks went by, and still I had not summoned sufficient courage to introduce myself. The following Sunday, the opportunity was placed directly in my lap. There was a special children's program in the worship service and the chapel was packed. I got there early and had a seat close to the front. She entered and took a seat behind me.

During the service, the church had a greeting custom. Everyone stood and introduced themselves to the people around them. When the time arrived, I took complete advantage of the opportunity. Turning around, I extended my hand. "Good morning. I'm Eric Crane."

"Hello, I'm Diana Lunden." Our eyes met and my heart rapidly pounded. "And these two are?"

"Will and Amy. Say hello to Ms. Lunden, kids."

"Hello." Amy was first. Will looked down at the floor.

"Shy." I spoke for him.

"Hi, Amy. What a pretty white dress."

"What do you say?" I asked Amy who had not learned how to accept a compliment.

"Thank you," she responded sheepishly.

The minister spoke. "Now, let's turn to page fifty-six in your hymnal and sing our welcome song."

We faced the pulpit, opened our hymnals and sang. For the balance of the service, I thought about Diana Lunden. I could hardly wait until the final prayer. After the worship service, coffee was served in the fellowship room. I stayed to talk to her.

That was the beginning. For the next few Sundays we spoke during the coffee hour following the worship service. I looked forward to our brief, though always interesting conversations. Eventually I gathered enough nerve to ask her out for dinner, and she accepted.

I picked her up at her place. Diana invited me in and offered me herbal tea, then went into the kitchen to get it. I looked at her home. Her living room was tastefully decorated, hardwood floors, a sofa, love seat, rocking chair and plants.

She returned with two cups of tea. "Please, have a seat," she said.

I sat on the rocking chair facing her, as she took her place on the love seat. I wanted to know more about the woman who had such a vibrant, ethereal presence.

"So Eric, tell me a little more about yourself." Diana spoke first.

Where should I begin, with Abliel or Vida? No, better save that for later. How about general stuff? I'm an alcoholic who's been married twice? Man, what a story!

"Okay. I consider myself to be a spiritual, although non-religious, person. I'm a member of Alcoholics Anonymous and have been in recovery for a few years." I decided to go straight to the heart of the matter.

"Oh yes, I'm familiar with AA. I have friends who are members."

"That's great, so you know it's a program that teaches us how to live life without the need for our addictions?"

"Yep." She nodded.

"Well, I sense incredible energy coming from you, from what I picked up on at church." Awkward at small talk, I feel more at ease by speaking what is on my mind.

"Yeah, well, when you look at me, I feel little zingers go 'zap'." She gestured with her thumb and finger.

"Zingers?" I had not heard it described like that.

"I'm very sensitive to energy. Yours is intense. Are you aware of it?"

"I am now."

"Now?" Diana's reply displayed her curiosity.

"Let's go to dinner and I'll explain." I offered with a smile.

"Sounds good to me."

We left for dinner. I had a favorite vegetarian restaurant in mind. We got a table outside in the courtyard where I told her my story.

Diana sat there, fork in hand, listening, but not eating. So I asked, "Don't you like the food?"

Startled, she snapped as though she had been awakened from a dream. "Oh, I'm sorry. I got so wrapped up in your story that I forgot." She quickly took a bite.

"That's okay, I guess. I was wondering if we should go somewhere else."

"No, no, this is fine. I'm so embarrassed." She took another bite. "But your story is so interesting, that I forgot about eating completely."

"Thanks." I didn't know what else to say, so I resumed my story.

Diana and I saw each other exclusively for several months. We saw movies, watched shows, viewed art exhibits, attended concerts and walked outdoors. I enjoyed her company. It was like having a friend with whom I could also be romantically involved.

I found myself growing concerned about the outcome of our relationship. In typical alcoholic fashion, I wanted something permanent, yet fear lurked in a remote outpost of my heart. I had been married twice, and even though Sonnie had passed away, the marriage died before she did. The last thing I wanted was to have a repeat performance in the relationship department.

The lessons I had learned from Abliel and Vida taught me one thing; I needed to be open and honest. I called my sponsor in AA and explained my feelings to him. "I don't want to get caught up in the same old stuff again," I explained.

"Okay, I see. Well, you know the drill. If you really care about this woman, then you've got to be rigorously honest. Check your motives, take an inventory. This whole thing isn't only about you, there's another human being involved here. You gotta do what's right for you, but you also have to respect her and her feelings. Being in a relationship is a two-way street. We've gotta get the 'me, me, me' out of it."

"Right." Over the past few years I had learned not to question Herbert. My job was simply to listen. I could do whatever I chose to do, but if I called him, I had to listen. Ten times out of ten, I did exactly as he instructed me.

"Here's what you do. Make a list of what you want in a relationship. Then write down what this relationship has to offer, compared to what's on that list. Then write down what you have to offer, compared to the list. And remember, you have to change your thoughts and your actions if you want this, or any, relationship to be different. A healthy relationship doesn't just happen. You have to want it to happen and then do something about it."

I followed his advice to the letter. I wrote the list. I found that I had some things that were important to me in a relationship, things that I questioned about Diana. Over the next few weeks, I tried to make sure that my thinking was clear. Eventually, I convinced myself that the only thing to do was to break it off with her. That's how most alcoholics think. If it doesn't work, throw it away. It's not worth fixing, especially when you can have something new.

Diana and I planned a long weekend away together. I was acting strangely, putting emotional distance between us. She knew something was wrong, but when she asked me what it was, I denied there was anything wrong and said I was tired. "Yeah, real original," I thought.

Finally, on the second day, our plans fell through due to inclement weather, and I found myself confronted with only the two of us. The time was then or never. Everything I had learned in the past few years was to be put to the test. I was through discussing being open and intimate with Vida. I had to put the theory to the test. I had to be open and intimate and honest in a relationship. I waited until the words almost forced themselves out. "Well, I guess I'm ready to tell you what's going on with me," I said solemnly.

Diana looked up from reading a magazine. "Okay."

"First, I want you to know that being this open to someone makes me scared, but I need to let you know what's going on inside me, because I've been thinking about where I am with this relationship. I've withdrawn from it."

"Withdrawn?" Diana looked at me with a question mark on her face.

For the next twenty minutes, I spilled my guts out. I told it all to her.

"You want to break it off?" Diana asked with bewilderment.

"I don't want to stop seeing you. I like you, and my feelings for you are deep and profound. What I'm feeling now is a sense of commitment and obligation that I'm emotionally uncomfortable with. We need to make a change in how we move forward, so that I'm comfortable. So we are both comfortable. How do you feel about it?" I looked deep within her eyes.

"I love you, Eric. I want this to work, but I'm not clear on what you want."

"I'm having difficulty clearly expressing what I want. My past patterns haven't been very successful. This time, I want to do things differently. I want to be sure that if I commit my life to someone, I have no reservations. I want to choose the relationship rather than need it. I want to be me, to be loved for who I am, no matter what. I want to truly make a commitment and have the other person make one too, not just say she's making one."

The conversation lasted a couple of hours. We agreed that we would make no decisions while we were feeling emotional.

Communication between us had been effective. We understood the other's point of view. I felt better, clearer and closer to Diana. I had opened up and risked losing her by being honest about my feelings. She had honored my feelings by not running away or criticizing, defending, or blaming me or acting out negatively.

In the weeks that followed, I found my feelings for Diana growing. I had been reluctant to say "I love you," because the words had lost their special meaning with Sonnie. But I was able to show my affection through my actions and by using other words. Inside, though, I was feeling love for her.

During the ensuing months I proved to myself that I could be open in a relationship. Like the rose, it took time and effort to cultivate. I had to work on it every day, but the effort was worth it. The old ways led to a certain fateful conclusion. The new way, being open, had unlimited possibilities.

Daily I worked to communicate honestly with Diana. If I was tired, I told her. She learned that after I rested, I would talk to her, and be completely present for the conversation. Communication in our relationship was a responsibility we shared with equal discipline.

I practiced listening to her. The more interest I took in her life, the more my love for her increased. I worked at doing little things for her out of a desire to make her life more joyful. I learned we were free to create the type of relationship we desired. The only things that could limit us were our thoughts.

With a commitment to be honest, open and emotionally present in the relationship, Diana and I had an adventure awaiting us. And that's another story.

ABOUT THE AUTHOR

Kenneth Byrd Chance is the founder and Executive Director of The Montana Society (Men of New Thought and New Awareness), a non-profit organization dedicated to the spiritual growth and personal development of men. His captivating style makes him a popular national speaker on topics related to recovery, relationships and spiritual transformation. He resides in Florida with his children.

For more information contact us at:

Rojaketaka Publications
8668 Navarre Parkway
Suite 110
Navarre, FL 32566
USA
www.rojaketaka.com